Unleashing the Power of Food

Recipes to Heal By

By FaXiang Hou

Published by
Agora Health Books
819 North Charles Street
Baltimore, Maryland 21201

Disclaimer
This book is informational only and is not intended to substitute for consultation with a medical doctor. Any attempt to diagnose and treat illness should take place under the direction of a physician. This book does not offer diagnoses or treatments. Nothing noted in this text should be considered an attempt by the author or publisher to practice medicine, prescribe remedies, or make diagnoses.

Published by
Agora Health Books
819 North Charles Street
Baltimore, Maryland 21201

ISBN 1-891434-08-X

Printed in the United States of America

Table of Contents
About Master FaXiang Hou
Introduction
Testimonials
Part One: Preliminaries

Part Two: Chinese Recipes for Health

Part Three: Sample Diet Plans

About Master FaXiang Hou

Master FaXiang Hou is a certified and highly accomplished Master of Medical QiGong and traditional Chinese medicine. In the tradition of many great Masters, his methods of healing QiGong, acupuncture, and herbal medicine have been passed down through his family for five generations. He and his brother are the only known recipients of a unique and powerful form of healing QiGong called "Ching Loong San Dian Xue Mi Gong Fa." At the age of 13, Master Hou began training under his father in these healing arts. As a young adult, he also studied under five other accomplished Masters in China. He has undergone rigorous clinical testing of his healing ability in China and has thereby been deemed a Certified Master in the elite International Qigong Science Association, as well as the Chinese QiGong Association.

Master Hou has had success treating a wide variety of chronic and acute ailments and diseases, including but not limited to: chronic headache and migraines, allergies, asthma, inflammatory conditions, insomnia, hypertension, gastro inflammation of the intestines, pneumonia, pulmonary emphysema, rheumatic arthritis, pleurisy, acute traumatic injuries, edema, strains, sprains, dislocations, gynecological conditions, strokes and neurological disorders, blood disorders, mastitis, and some non-metastasized cancers, vertebral conditions, chronic-fatigue syndrome, and immune-system enhancing, along with relief of the symptomatology in HIV/AIDS.

Master Hou is currently the Director of The QiGong Research Society in Mount Laurel, New Jersey, and holds private consultations in Cherry Hill, New Jersey.

Foreward

This book by Master FaXiang Hou covers an aspect of health and healing which is often overlooked in the American culture. We all require food to nourish our bodies but few of us know how to use food to heal our bodies. In addition to his unusual healing abilities, he is outstanding chef and extremely knowledgeable in the Chinese way of using food and combinations of foods and nutrients to establish the balance that nature provides us with.

I am pleased that he has chosen to pass some of this knowledge on to readers and students. His diet plans and recipes are easy to follow and the ingredients readily obtainable. We all have a great source of untapped energy within us, some of which can be unleashed through the power of food.

Steven Seagal
Actor, writer, director, and producer

Introduction

When I was a younger man, I paid little attention to diet and nutrition. Because I was healthy and in good physical condition, I didn't believe that a bad diet could affect me. As I got older, however, I noticed that my own physical health was starting to break down, and I even began to show many of the same symptoms as my patients had.

Since then, I've become more concerned about my diet and have followed the ways of traditional Chinese longevity. I've spent four decades studying nutrition, the effects of food on the body, and Chinese cooking for health. This is all in addition to my regular practice as an energy healer.

I've tried to pass on much of this knowledge to my patients and students in hopes that they'll learn the nutritional value of food. I've tried to help them identify what foods are right for them individually as well as the proper cooking methods for those foods. Unfortunately, my time is very limited due to my growing healing practice and I can't counsel as many people as I would like. Hence this book.

Though I am neither a fancy chef nor a great writer, I decided to write this book so that more of you might understand the important role food plays in your health and thus improve your own dietary choices.

We eat everyday in order to satisfy our hunger and quench our thirst. But the food we consume does so much more than this. Food actually acts as a kind of medicine. And unlike many of the traditional medicines used to cure illnesses, food can actually prevent them.

Oriental cooking, especially Chinese, is completely different from Western cooking in its background, materials, and methods.

Indeed, the Chinese philosophy of food has much to offer the American palate and American health. Throughout their history, the Chinese have placed much emphasis on food as a means of maintaining health. As early as 2500 B.C., they had developed a systematic theory linking food to physical well-being. They believe that food works much like medicine. And though it may work more slowly than medicine, food still plays a crucial role in illness prevention and long-term cures.

This makes intuitive sense. It has been proven time and again that, regardless of the particular illness involved, when patients take a proactive approach in terms of their dietary intake, their diseases take a favorable turn after only two weeks. The patients become physically stronger, and their pathogenic symptoms begin to abate.

The Chinese believe that the spleen (pi) and stomach (wei) digest and absorb nutrition. This belief holds that good health depends on keeping the spleen and stomach in good condition through the eating of proper foods. Food, therefore really acts as a slow-acting medicine with no negative side effects.

Chinese food consists mainly of plant foods and features low-fat, low-calorie, and high-fiber dishes. This is why China's rates of hypertension, diabetes, and obesity fall far short of those of (advanced) countries like the United States.

Preparation is vastly different between East and West. In preparing meals, the Chinese try to combine complementary ingredients. They want to harmonize the ingredients to help prevent and relieve different conditions. Turnip, for example, is usually prepared with lamb or beef, as turnip is considered a "cool" food while lamb and beef are considered "warm" in nature.

When you combine them, the heat within beef or lamb is greatly reduced by the turnip, therefore making the dish "calm," and thus healthier and easier to digest. Also, the Chinese usually heat oil before adding ingredients to it. This simple process burns much of the fat from the oil before food even goes into it. A more detailed discussion of these ideas will follow in Chapter 1.

In this book, I have attempted to include recipes that can be easily understood and prepared by mainstream Americans. Still, some may seem strange to the reader. But don't let their exotic nature confuse you. Most of them have been in China for a long time. Some of the recipes provide fast, easy, and tasty ways to properly nourish your body, others describe traditional dishes from the various regions in China, and still others are designed for entertaining. In many cases, their value in keeping people healthy has been proven scientifically. They have been selected because they are commonly seen on Chinese restaurant menus and family dinner tables, because they are easy to prepare and because they taste good.

In some places, I have altered basic recipes in order to lower calories, salt, or fat content and maintain high nutritional standards and healing properties. I personally use these recipes and recommend them to my patients regularly as an excellent assistance to healing therapies. In order to reap the most benefit from the recipes, I strongly suggest using only fresh, organic foods.

Please keep in mind, however, that food should not be substituted for medicine when a condition already exists. I don't want anyone to misunderstand the healing power of food alone. Medically speaking, food can only assist in the healing process. In other words, though carrots contain betacarotene, which is good for eyesight, eating a bag of carrots will not heal cataracts. And, of course, you should never discontinue the use of prescription medications without discussing it with your physician first. The prevention of illness and maintenance of health rely on many factors. Food, though an extremely important factor, is only one of them.

My suggestion for using this book is very simple: Engage in physical and mental exercise, select and combine the proper foods, and cook them in the right way. By doing so, you can prevent many illnesses and greatly reduce or even reverse those that are already within you.

This book is divided into three sections. Part One, "Preliminaries," provides an introduction to the Chinese medical concept of food and outlines the health benefits of each food group. Part Two, "Chinese Recipes for Health," provides more than 200 recipes to help heal and prevent illness. Part Three, "Sample Diet Plans," offers a detailed list of foods to eat or avoid for common ailments. In addition, it contains specific diet plans for hypertension, diabetes, obesity, heart diseases, and cancer. By incorporating the recipes and using these plans as guidelines, readers can create additional diet plans to meet their individual needs.

To me, cooking is both an art and a science. If you start cooking and eating healthy, gradually your body will get used to a good diet and will automatically avoid junk food. You will begin to lean toward what your body needs and your body will "learn" how to tell you what it wants. You need only start by eating better food, and this cookbook will put you on that path.

I would like to extend my thanks to Eric Yin, who helped me to collect and translate all the material for this book; to Mark V. Wiley for editing, revising, and preparing the book for publishing; and to Anne Kelly and Agora Health Books for their enthusiasm in this project and willingness to publish it.

—Master FaXiang Hou

Mount Laurel, New Jersey

PART ONE:
Preliminaries

CHAPTER 1
We Are What We Eat

Few Americans consider the direct connection between food and their health. Food is simply thought of as either basic fuel, or worse, a tasty form of entertainment. In fact, however, food does have a direct effect on our health; it has the power to poison or invigorate. Food can operate in your system like a weight upon your body or power you to higher energy like high-octane fuel. Like medicine, the proper foods can help cure many illnesses. A relatively simple change in diet can often alter or even halt the disease process. By choosing the right foods, we can restore our energy, vitality, and good health.

Western doctors prescribe medications in reaction to illnesses their patients suffer from. The medicines are used to cure or treat existing diseases. Few physicians realize that carefully selected foods can be used medicinally to heal or treat the sick as well. Even fewer doctors understand that foods have a healing energy that goes well beyond the scope of traditional Western medicine. By eating the right foods in the right combinations, we have the power to prevent disease and illness from ever occurring.

The Chinese have understood this connection between food and illness for thousands of years. The concept that what we eat directly influences how we feel is a basic building block of Chinese medicine. Indeed, the Chinese concept of balanced nutrition has much to teach the West. Food is selected and prepared according to specific guidelines that allow the natural ability of foods to prevent and heal illness to be harnessed for our own benefit. The success of these dietary techniques is illustrated in the many centuries of vibrant health that the Chinese have enjoyed.

Few people would question that certain kinds of foods can cause illnesses, including hypertension, coronary heart disease, diabetes, and ulcers. We need look no further than the typical American high-fat animal-based diet for an example of this connection. In fact, Americans generally get about a third of their daily caloric intake from animal-based foods, and animal protein makes up 70 percent of their total protein intake. The results of this ill-advised diet are illustrated by the dramatic rise in obesity, hypertension, heart disease, and diabetes in the West.

Just as eating the wrong foods can lead to illness, eating the right ones can lead to good health. A simple guideline for determining how healthy a food is to access how "plain" it is. In other words the more basic or pure a food is, the less processing it has gone through, the healthier it is for you. Traditionally, the

Chinese daily diet is made up of plain foods like grains and vegetables. Many of the diseases plaguing the Western World are almost nonexistent in China.

The Chinese recognized a connection between food and illness long ago. There are dozens of ancient books in China dedicated to dietary concerns and proper eating habits. Some of these basic guidelines have remained virtually unchanged for centuries, such as understanding the benefits of eating meals at regular times, curbing overeating, and avoiding eating only one type of food. The connection between food and health was actually suggested as long as 2,000 years ago, when the Chinese book *Lushi Chunqiu* informed people that, "thick and pungent tastes are the incentives of illness." Greasy, deep-fried, and pungent foods, the book said, can "promote the production of phlegm and create dumpiness; raise liver's yang and invite liver's wind."

Despite the fact that the health benefits of a plant-based diet are already well understood in the West, this knowledge seems rarely put into use by Americans. Compound carbohydrates like rice and corn help lower cholesterol and lead to a lower chance of developing coronary heart disease. Vegetables, which contain high amounts of vitamins and minerals and moderate amounts of protein, fat, and sugar, are practically perfect foods, with a long list of health benefits:

- Vegetables stimulate the digestive glands and promote improved digestion and absorption.
- Vegetables, which are low in calories, promote weight loss, which can reverse or prevent a number of obesity-related illnesses.
- The acids in certain vegetables may be able to keep sugar from turning into fat.
- Vegetables contain more cellulose than most foods do, and cellulose can improve intestinal function.
- Vegetables help prevent or cure cardiovascular disease.
- Most vegetables contain a large amount of potassium, which the heart needs to function properly.
- Vegetables contain large amounts of fiber.
- Eating more vegetables can help prevent cancer.
- Enzymes in pumpkin, bean sprouts, and asparagus and the lignin in sweet potatoes, radishes, and potatoes can eliminate carcinogens from the body.
- Plant oils distilled from peanuts, vegetable seeds, and beans contain unsaturated fatty acids, which have been proven to lower cholesterol.
- For those suffering from clogged arteries, the pectin in vegetables can help remove excess cholesterol from the blood.

I urge my patients, and all Americans, to think as the Chinese do about food. The too-often-ignored cliché "You are what you eat" is rooted in the truth. Food can poison our bodies or lead us to perfect health. The choice is yours. You have the power to control your health and how you feel by what you choose to put into your mouth.

CHAPTER 2
An Introduction to Traditional Chinese Medicine

Some of the concepts I will discuss in this chapter may, at first, seem foreign or difficult to understand. However, these beliefs are fundamental to the secrets of Chinese health and longevity. In traditional Chinese medicine, the individual is seen as part of a bigger picture — part of the natural universe. The theories that follow illustrate the belief that we are, just as the universe is, controlled by certain rules of nature. The Chinese believe that the body, like the rest of nature, can be understood, and even manipulated, once this framework that defines the natural world is understood. As you read through this book, you will begin to see how these concepts work hand in hand with the provided recipes and food guidelines in order to help you take control of your own health and well-being.

Yin and Yang Balance in the Body

I touched on the systematic theory that links food to physical well-being in the last chapter. This concept is a basic building block of traditional Chinese medicine. Another integral aspect of traditional Chinese Medicine is emphasis on balance. The theory of balance, which involves both yin (negative elements) and yang (positive elements), influences an entire view of the world. The theory of yin and yang holds that all things have an opposite yet complementary aspect. These two sides should not be thought of in terms of a Western sense of good and bad. Rather, it should be understood that they are dependent on each other for their very existence. After all, there is no hot without cold, no joy without sorrow, and no play without work. Thus, the balance between yin and yang represents a universal law of the material world. While these two aspects are in opposition to each other, because one end of the spectrum cannot exist without the other, they are also dependent on each other. The words "yin" and "yang" really describe a character more than anything strictly material. "Yin" represents water, quiet, substance, and night. "Yang" represents fire, noise, function, and day.

The human body is, as are all things, a balance of yin and yang. In Chinese medicine, it is taught that the body's five main organs — the heart, lungs, kidneys, liver, and spleen — regulate and control the body's major functions and its general health. The Chinese call these five main organs the 'zang', or solid organs. The Chinese medical model gives these organs a great deal more power and responsibility than Western science does. All remaining organs are secondary to them and largely controlled by them.

17

The energy flow among the five zang organs controls the delicate yin/yang balance of the body. Each of the solid organs of the body contains an element of yin and an element of yang. Some organs contain more yang, others more yin. In the healthy body, the yin/yang properties within are in a constantly fluctuating yet continual balance. When yin and yang go out of balance in a body, poor health generally follows. To restore your body to good health, you need to ensure that your body is returned to a balanced state. You can achieve this state of balance for your body through the proper selection, preparation, and eating of foods.

In winter, for example, a practitioner of Chinese medicine would suggest eating more nutritious foods. Much energy has been expended during the prior three seasons, and replenishing the body during the winter months will restore balance. Also, the lower temperatures of winter requires a higher caloric intake — just for the purpose of keeping the body warm.

Women who have just given birth provide another perfect illustration of this need to restore balance in the body. A woman who has just given birth has used up much of her vital energy (qi). During her recovery time she will need to eat highly nutritious foods to restore the yin/yang balance of her system.

In Chinese medicine, it is taught that after food leaves the stomach it is directed to certain organs based on the taste of the particular food; sour food goes to the liver, bitter food goes to the heart, sweet food goes to the spleen, pungent food goes to the lung, and salty food goes to the kidney. Based on this theory, it is clear to see how diet can disrupt the yin and yang balance among the organs of the body. The five "tastes" should be coordinated, and one's diet should not be heavily biased toward one taste at the expense of others. In short, a balance of yin and yang through proper selection, combining, and preparation of food is crucial to maintaining optimal health. The five tastes, as well as the four properties of foods and how they affect our internal balance and health, are discussed in more detail later in this chapter.

The Five-elements Theory

The five elements refer to five categories of material found in the natural world: wood, fire, earth, metal, and water. The theory of the five elements holds that all phenomena in the universe correspond in nature to wood, fire, earth, metal or water, and that these are in a state of constant motion and change as they interact with one another.

The theory of the five elements was formed in China at about the time of the Yin and Zhou dynasties (16th century-221 B.C.). Historically, the theory was derived from observations of the natural world made by the Chinese people in the course of their daily lives.

Wood, fire, earth, metal, and water were considered to be indispensable materials for maintaining a productive life. It was also understood that these elements were important to initiating normal changes in the natural world.

When we eat food, we are linked with the elements of the outside world. For optimal health, meals should be varied according to the changes of time and season. The Chinese believe, for example, that foods contain more sour substances in the spring, bitter substances in the summer, pungent substances in the fall and salty substances in the winter. Proper seasonings should be used to dilute the tastes of certain foods to avoid harming the body.

Food's Four Properties and Five Tastes

In Chinese medicine, food is categorized according to particular properties and tastes. Understanding them will help you maintain the yin and yang balance in your body. First, we'll talk about the way the Chinese categorize food. Then we'll talk about how to keep all these food values in balance.

In Chinese medicine, a food can be catalogued according to its cold, hot, warm, cool, or neutral energy as well as its taste. You can cause an imbalance in your body if you eat too much food with a particular kind of energy. In order to decide what kind of food your body needs, you must take into account your own body type. Body types hold a particular importance in Chinese medicine, as I'll discuss later on.

First, however, let's go over the taste categories. The five categories of taste are sour, bitter, sweet, pungent, and salty. Generally, a food falls into one of these categories depending upon how the tongue perceives it. As I discussed earlier, the Chinese believe food, depending on its taste, will go to one of the five organs when it leaves the stomach. We must choose foods according to our current state of health. If too much food of any one particular taste is eaten, you risk disrupting the yin and yang balance of your body which can lead to illness.

Modifying a given food's taste value by using spices or complementary foods can reduce this risk of disturbing the yin and yang balance. The ancient book *Food Cures* advises, for example, that "beef goes with rice, lamb goes with millet, chicken goes with wheat, pork goes with millet, fish goes with melons, etc." Thus, since beef is sweet in "taste" and "neutral" in nature and rice is bitter in "taste" and "warm" in nature, combining these two can neutralize the bitter and sweet to make the meal a moderate one and thus easier for the body to digest.

Body Types and Health

Let's get back to a food's energy values now and the problem of how to keep them in balance in the body. The Chinese sort bodies into three different categories and six different body types: hot and cold bodies, excessive and deficient bodies, and dry and damp bodies. Each body type can achieve and maintain balance through the sort of food appropriate to that particular body type.

For example, some people sweat heavily after eating pungent foods. People with this kind of body type benefit from eating cold foods like fruits and melons. If, however, you have a cold body type, you should avoid cold foods and instead choose hot foods, such as scallions, chives, garlic, and pepper. The body's "temperature" bias should be in line with the energy property of food. "Cold" bodies balance "hot" foods, and vice versa. Each body type has its own dietary needs.

It should be noted that traditional Chinese medicine recognizes individual dietary needs, and understands that proper food selection must take an individual's particular case into account.

Hot and Cold Bodies

Those with a hot body type are often anxious and easily excited. They may also be somewhat aggressive. Hot body types suffer from excessive thirst (preferring cold drinks)and hyperemia (an excess of blood in a body part). If you are a hot body type, you can expect a low volume of yellow-colored urine.

Cold body types often suffer from low energy and feelings of general poor health. They seldom feel thirsty (preferring hot drinks), excrete almost clear urine, and have a tendency towards anemia.

Excessive and Deficient Bodies

The excessive body type is able to kill off viruses and other illness. People of this type are often very strong and produce less sweat.

The deficient body type can fight off a virus but is often too weak to kill one once infected. People of this type are often weak and powerless, tend to sweat more, and appear thin and pale.

Dry and Damp Bodies

Dry bodies tend to hold less body fluid and are usually characterized by a dry cough. Their bodies are dry, and they always feel thirsty.

Damp bodies tend to maintain excessive body fluids; get diseases like hypertension, edema, and diarrhea; and have noisy stomachs.

Food Properties and Health

Have you noticed how the food types and body types correspond? You can correct a coldness of the body, for example, by eating warm or hot foods, and you can correct a hotness of the body by eating cool or cold foods. If a person with a hot or excessive body type eats too many hot foods, he may suffer from hyperemia, hypertension, or inflammation.

Certainly, it's not easy to recognize a perfect one-to-one correspondence between body type and food type. But we can roughly figure out how they relate: Hot and warm foods benefit cold, deficient, and damp bodies, while cold and cool foods benefit hot, excessive, and dry bodies.

Now that you have been introduced to the basic principles of traditional Chinese medicine, you should have a better understanding of how to use food as a tool to improve your health and prevent illness. My hope is that you will now be able to determine which food choices are best for your body type and specific health situation. With this book as a guide, you will be well on your way to a healthier, balanced lifestyle.

CHAPTER 3
How to Use This Book

In order for you to get the most benefit from this cookbook, I have dedicated an entire chapter to explaining how to use it properly. If you were to visit me in my office, I no doubt would bend your ear with endless stories of how eating this way has completely turned around the lives of many of my patients. However, since I am unable to sit down with each of you personally, this book is the next-best thing. Using a simple, easy-to-follow format, I will walk you through your journey toward good health.

Chapter 4, "Food Nutrition and Healing Properties," provides a comprehensive, alphabetical guide to the properties of individual foods. I discuss the general nutritional content and — most importantly — the therapeutic character of each food.

Since I can't be there to advise you on specific food choices, I designed chapter 4 to be used as a quick-reference tool. The sections are laid out so you can quickly locate an individual food and see, at a glance, all you need to know about it. You can also use this section as a guide to creating your own health-promoting dishes.

In Chapter 5, "Chinese Recipes for Health," I have collected my favorite recipes to share with you. Each recipe includes step-by-step instructions. As a reminder that food, like medicine, can be used to heal and maintain good health, each recipe includes a section that details the medicinal uses of the dish. I also use symbols to point out the best recipes for curing and preventing the most common illnesses we suffer from today. I encourage you to flip through and find what recipes work best for your own particular illness or that of a loved one.

I have included a chart below of the symbols I have used and what each one means:

Hypertension	⊛
Diabetes	✳
Weight loss/obesity	�
Heart disease	☯
Cancer	⛰

My recipes are designed to be flexible; you may personalize them according to your own tastes and needs. You will find that a number of my recipes call for green onion or garlic ships, which are prepared by cutting the onion or garlic into very thin slices. If you prefer you can crush the garlic or chop the onions into larger chunks. Go ahead and experiment and find out what works best for you. In recipes that call for oil I recommend using any oil that does not contain preservatives including flax seed, sesame, sunflower, or olive oils. When starch is listed as an ingredient feel free to use corn yam, or bean starches. And natural sweeteners found in any health food store can easily modify any of my recipes that include sugar.

I start Chapter 6, "Sample Diet Plans", with a helpful chart of 15 common ailments, the foods you should choose to treat them, and the foods you should avoid.

A more in-depth look is then given to some of the more common illnesses that plague the Western World. Specific advice is offered for each ailment, and each is accompanied by a disease-specific daily diet plan. Please note that I have not included a daily diet plan for arthritis. Arthritis, unlike the other diseases I have discussed in this book, is not as directly related to the foods we eat. A true diet plan that would cover all the different types and aspects of arthritis would be impossible. If you do suffer from arthritis or painful joints you will find a number of recipes in Chapter 5 that may help to relieve your symptoms. Experiment to find out which ones work the best for you.

Now that you know how to use my cookbook, here are some tips on how to ensure you get the most nutritional benefit out of the dishes you make. Keep in mind that most of my recipes call for the use of a wok. The Chinese like to spend less time cooking meals and more time enjoying them. Using a wok, most of my recipes can be prepared in 20 minutes or less, leaving you more time to spend with your family and friends. I also prefer to use the wok because it gets hot in a quicker period of time than a normal pan and cooks food faster, sealing in more of its nutritional value. However, you can use an iron skillet and achieve similar results.

Proper Food Combinations and Cooking Methods

In traditional Chinese medicine, how foods are combined is very important. In fact, the 3000-year-old Chinese book *Neijin* says that "to combine the five tastes properly can strengthen bones and soften tendon; improve the circulation of vital energy (qi) and blood." In other words, a diverse diet is important because single foods cannot provide the range of nutrients a human body needs to remain healthy.

Here's a quick summary of what basic nutrients the healthy body needs and what foods we need to eat to get them:

- Most grains contain starch, sugar, protein, and thiamine.
- Animal foods and beans contain protein and fat.
- Vegetables provide vitamins, mineral salt and rough fibers.

Traditionally, the Chinese cook will combine foods based on a simple, almost elementary, formula: Combine coarse food grains (for example maize, sorghum, millet, etc.) with fine food grains (for example wheat and rice) and combine dry foods with watery foods. I will discuss food combinations more in a bit.

First, let's get to the bigger question of how to cook these foods. Over our long history, the Chinese have developed distinct and specific cooking methods that avoid the common unhealthy pitfalls of Western cooking. The Chinese cooking and preparation methods, such as the ones I list below, focus on retaining foods' inherent nutritional value.

- **Avoid heavy washing of grains and vegetables.**

Rice and wheat flour, which provide starch, protein, Vitamin B, and mineral salt to our diet, are the primary sources of food for the Chinese people. You should avoid heavy washing of wheat and rice, because much of their nutritional content — Vitamin B in particular — resides on the grains surface. The heavy rinsing of rice, for example, can eliminate up to 15 percent of the mineral content, 40 percent of the vitamin B content, and 10 percent of the protein content.

The nutritional content of vegetables is concentrated in their skin, which often is high in Vitamin C. I suggest washing vegetables lightly and never soaking them in water, especially after cutting.

Since vegetables contain a high volume of vitamins and mineral salt, it is best to choose fresh and organic ones whenever possible. Organic vegetables are far less likely to be treated with pesticides and preservatives, and they therefore require less washing.

- **Cook vegetables to keep nutrients in.**

The best way to cook vegetables is to sauté them over high heat. The cooking time should be as short as possible to keep the vitamins inside from being destroyed. Boiling is not ordinarily a healthy method of cooking; however, boiling in moderation is fine. Make sure to cover the pot or pan during boiling, which should help prevent the escape of vitamin B-1 and vitamin C through evaporation.

When cooking vegetables, use a little vinegar and starch in order to help protect the vitamin C content.

• **Cook meat to make it tender.**

Meat and other animal products are usually hard to digest. To make them easier to digest, they should be cooked until tender. If you insist upon adding salt for taste, avoid doing this as long as possible in the cooking process. Salt shortens cooking times and ultimately can cause the meat to be tough.

Whenever possible, mix meat with soy sauce or starch before cooking it in a wok. This makes the meat tender and tastier and protects the vitamins and proteins from being cooked away.

When you cook dishes that combine foods, especially vegetables and meats, it's important to begin cooking each food at the right time, and to cook it for the right duration. My recipes include specific instructions as to the proper cooking times and the proper "dropping order." You should follow the recipes carefully, as they are designed to maximize the healthy properties of each dish.

Proper Eating Habits

Three meals a day, spaced five to six hours apart, will provide the body with all the nutrients it needs and with enough time to digest the food between meals. A Chinese idiom holds that we should "eat better food in breakfast, eat fully in lunch, and eat less in dinner."

Breakfast should provide 30 percent to 35 percent of your daily calories, lunch should provide 40 percent of your calories, and dinner should provide 25 percent to 30 percent of your calories. In the morning, most people need plenty of calories to get going; their appetites, however, are not usually big. Small portions of higher-calorie foods work best for breakfast, which should be eaten at around 7 or 8 a.m.

Lunch should replenish the morning's consumption of energy while preparing the body for the afternoon. It should be the highest-calorie meal of the day. Foods relatively high in protein and fat are recommended. It should be eaten around noon.

For dinner, eat cooked vegetables and other easily digested foods. As our physical activities diminish in the evening, we need fewer calories. Eating heavier at dinner leads to the storing of nutrients in the body in the form of fat, which can contribute to obesity and its related illnesses. A rich dinner will also give the stomach and intestines more work to do, causing abdominal distension and perhaps disturbing sleep. Traditional Chinese medicine holds that going to bed with a full stomach may lead to various diseases, due to indigestion and food coagulation. Dinner should be eaten at around 6:30 to 7:30 p.m. Please remember to wait at least one hour before going to bed.

Now that I have armed you with the knowledge of how food can be used to treat and prevent illness, you are prepared to begin your journey toward good health. I hope you enjoy my recipes as much as I enjoyed writing them down for you. Remember, there is truth in the old adage "You are what you eat."

CHAPTER 4
Individual Food Nutrition & Healing Properties

MEAT

Beef:
- Properties: Sweet, warm
- Nutritional Contents: Protein, fat, sugar, vitamins A and B, mineral salt, niacin
- Therapeutic Actions: Replenishes vital energy, strengthens spleen and nourishes stomach, strengthens bones and muscles and promotes the circulation of body fluid to relieve swelling.

Lamb:
- Properties: Sweet, hot
- Nutritional Contents: Protein, fat, sugar, mineral salt, vitamins A, B, C and niacin, calcium, iron
- Therapeutic Actions: A very good tonic for general fatigue, also applied to lung diseases and anemia.

Pork:
- Properties: Sweet and salty, neutral
- Nutritional Contents: Protein, fat
- Therapeutic Actions: Nourishes blood vessels, lubricates muscles and skin.

POULTRY

Chicken:
- Properties: Sweet and salty, neutral
- Nutritional Contents: protein, magnesium, potassium
- Therapeutic Actions: Tonifies the five organs, nourishes the spleen and stomach, strengthens muscles and bones, promotes blood circulation and regulates menstruation.

Duck:
- Properties: Sweet and salty, slightly cold
- Nutritional Contents: Protein, fat
- Therapeutic Actions: Nourishes yin, restores deficiency, stops cough, promotes circulation of body fluids and resolves phlegm.

29

DAIRY

Chicken Egg:
- Properties: Neutral, sweet
- Nutritional Contents: Protein, carotene, vitamin B1, B2, phosphate, iron, calcium
- Therapeutic Actions: It replenishes blood, relieves dryness and reinvigorates vital energy. It helps relieve general fatigue, especially for women after giving birth.
- Caution: Egg yolk contains high cholesterol.

Milk:
- Properties: Sweet, neutral to slightly warm
- Nutritional Contents: Protein, lactin, fat, calcium, phosphate, vitamin A, B1, B2, C, D.
- Therapeutic Actions: It greatly nourishes blood and vital energy to remove fatigue, nourishes skin and hair, moisturizes the lungs and improves vision.

SEAFOOD

Carp:
- Properties: Sweet, warm
- Nutritional Contents: Protein, fat, mineral salt, vitamin A, B, niacin
- Therapeutic Actions: Warms interior, promotes the circulation of body fluid to relieve swelling.

Ocean Crab:
- Properties: Salty, cold
- Nutritional Contents: Protein, fat, lecithinum, vitamins B1, B2, phosphate and iron
- Therapeutic Actions: Acts as a liver and stomach tonic, activates blood, cools heat sensations, and facilitates recovery of dislocations.
- Cautions: Because of its cold nature, it is not applied to stomach deficiency due to dampness and cold. Those with gout should not eat crab, as it is too high in protein.

Crucian:
- Properties: Sweet, neutral
- Nutritional Contents: Protein, fat, calcium, iron, phosphate, vitamins A, B, and niacin
- Therapeutic Actions: Promotes the production of body fluid, strengthens stomach. Especially used to promote milk production for women after-delivery.

Eel:
- Properties: Sweet, neutral
- Nutritional Contents: Protein, fat, vitamin A
- Therapeutic Actions: Can be used for lung diseases.
- Cautions: Do not eat excessive amounts of eel.

Kelp:
- Properties: Cold, salty
- Nutritional Contents:
- Therapeutic Actions: Replenishes blood and removes phlegm and other stasis. It can soften body hardness, clear vessels, remove heat and promote body fluid's circulation. This food is applied to cardiovascular diseases, diabetes.

Shrimp (including dried shrimp):
- Properties: Sweet, warm
- Nutritional Contents: Protein, fat, lecithinum, vitamin B1, B2, phosphate and iron
- Therapeutic Actions: Invigorates the kidney to enhance yang, is applied to impotence, fatigue and lassitude in the loins and knees due to deficiency of kidney. It can also promote the production of milk, and clear away toxins (such as erysipelas, ulcer).
- Cautions: Eating too much will enhance interior heat, and those with gout should eat shrimp, as it is high in protein.

Soft Shell Turtle:
- Properties: Salty, neutral
- Nutritional Contents: Protein, fat, sugar, niacin, mineral salt, vitamin B1, B2.
- Therapeutic Actions: Nourish yin and suppress yang, resolves stasis. Used for archoptosis, prolapse of the uterus.
- Cautions: Do not overeat, or you can hurt the stomach. It is counter-productive to poor appetite and indigestion.

VEGETABLES

Alfalfa Sprouts:
- Properties: Cool, bitter
- Nutritional Contents:
- Therapeutic Actions: Stomach and spleen tonic, it expels dampness and lubricates intestines.

Asparagus:
- Properties: Cool, sweet & bitter:

- Nutritional Contents: Vitamin C, vitamin B6, folacin, fiber
- Therapeutic Actions: It clears heat, expels dampness and relieves dryness. It can be used as diaphoretic to relieve water retension.

Bamboo Shoots:
- Properties: Sweet, cold
- Nutritional Contents: Vitamin C, phosphate, coarse fiber, and calcium
- Therapeutic Actions: It clears interior heat, can be used to detoxify, and is often used to balance warm energy of meat. It is a very good food for cardio-vascular diseases, diabetes and obesity.
- Caution: Be careful of its cold nature.

Bitter melon:
- Properties: Bitter, cold
- Nutritional Contents & Therapeutic Actions: Modern science has discovered that bitter melon is a very good food for many diseases: 1. Diabetes: The bitter melon fruit is widely used as food as well as medicine in Asia. The bitter melon is an anti-diabetic, which has been shown to increase the number of beta cells by the pancreas, thereby improving the body's ability to produce insulin. It is one of the few agents, which has the potential to bolster a flagging pancreas. At least three different ingredients in bitter melon have been reported to have hypoglycemic (blood-sugar-lowering) actions of potential benefit in diabetes mellitus. These include a mixture of steroidal saponins know as charantin, insulin-like peptides, and alkaloids. The bitter melon has been shown to improve glucose tolerance in Type II diabetes patients. The active agents in bitter melon are believed to be oleanolic acid glycosides, and momordins, which prevent absorption of sugar from the intestine. 2. HIV Infection: MAP 30 is a protein found in the bitter melon that is useful in treating HIV infection.

Carrot:
- Properties: Sweet, slight warm
- Nutritional Contents: Carotene, sugar, vitamin C, protein, fat, volatile oil, and minerals
- Therapeutic Actions: Reinvigorates stomach to improve digestion, dispels worms, helps vision, lowers blood pressure and accelerates the discharge of mercury from body.

Celery:
- Properties: Sweet, cold

- Nutritional Contents: Protein, fat, carbohydrate, vitamins, calcium, phosphate, iron
- Therapeutic Actions: Cleans stomach to remove heat, cleans and protects blood vessels, dispels wind to lubricate throat, helps vision and clears nose.

Chinese Cabbage (Nappa):
- Properties: Sweet, neutral and slightly cold
- Nutritional Contents: Vitamin C, B1, B2, U, and carotene.
- Therapeutic Actions: Stomach and liver tonic, promotes digestion and urination, nourishes kidney and brain, cleans stomach and intestines, smoothes chest and relieves restlessness, and improves digestion It can be used to treat Gastro duodenal ulcer.
- Caution: Those with ulcers or gastritis should be careful to not overeat.

Corn:
- Properties: Sweet, neutral
- Nutritional Contents: Glutamic acid, amylaceum, maize acid, apple acid, citrin, dihydroxysccinic acid, oxalic acid, resin, vitamin K
- Therapeutic Actions: Improves urination, nourishes spleen, arrests bleeding and lowers blood pressure and cholesterol. It can be used to treat cardiovascular diseases.

Chinese Prickly Ash:
- Properties: Pungent, warm
- Nutritional Contents: Volatile oil, unsaturated organic acid
- Therapeutic Actions: Reinvigorates stomach, removes worms, warms interior.

Chives:
- Properties: Sweet, warm
- Nutritional Contents: Volatile oil, sulfonium compound, protein, fat, sugar, vitamin B, C, and fiber
- Therapeutic Actions: Reinvigorates stomach and kidney, resolves extravagated blood, improves digestion and detoxifies body. It is applied to impotence, premature ejaculation, inflammation of the intestines, and dysentery.

Cucumber:
- Properties: Sweet, cold
- Nutritional Contents: Vitamin B1, B2, niacin, protein, sugar.
- Therapeutic Actions: Clears away heat to quench thirst, improves urination to remove swelling, lowers cholesterol and blood pressure.

Eggplant:
- Properties: Sweet, cold
- Nutritional Contents: Vitamin B, C, niacin, carotene, protein, fat.
- Therapeutic Actions: Resolves extravagated blood and stops pain, removes swelling and cleans intestines. The niacin can effectively protect capillaries. Eggplant is used to treat hypertension, arteriosclerosis, peliosis and scorbutus.

Green Bean Sprouts:
- Properties: Sweet, cool
- Nutritional Contents: Protein, vitamin C
- Therapeutic Actions: The nutritious value of green been sprouts is less than yellow bean sprouts, but they are much more tender and easier to digest. They also can clear more interior heat than yellow bean sprouts.

Hot Peppers:
- Properties: Pungent, hot
- Nutritional Contents: Capsaicin, capsicidin, protein, carotene, fat oil, vitamin C and volatile oil
- Therapeutic Actions: Stimulates the production of saliva and stomach acid, and can be used for cold stomach and rheumatalgia.
- Cautions: Counterproductive for chronic stomach diseases, tuberculosis, hypertension, toothache, hemorrhoids and swelling.

Kelp:
- Properties: Salty, cold
- Nutritional Contents: Iodine, carotene, vitamin B1, B2, protein, fat, sugar, chlorophyll, iron, cobalt, and arsenic
- Therapeutic Actions: Soften hardness and induces urination, replenishes blood and lowers cholesterol. It is used to treat enlargement of the thyroid gland, hypertension and vascular sclerosis.
- Caution: Not for cold stomach.

Leek:
- Properties: Pungent, warm
- Nutritional Contents: Vitamin C, fiber, protein, and phosphate
- Therapeutic Actions: It is a liver and lung tonic, removes blood stagnation, expels coldness, sedates yin, clears stomach fire (interior heat).
- Cautions: Leek can be irritating, and it is counter productive to stomach and intestine diseases and cancer.

Lotus Root:
- Properties: Sweet, cold (rare), warm (cooked)
- Nutritional Contents: Vitamin C, fiber
- Therapeutic Actions: Rare lotus root: remove stasis and cool blood, clear away heat and eliminate restlessness, whet appetite. Cooked lotus root: nourish spleen and stomach.

Mushroom:
- Properties: Sweet, cool
- Nutritional Contents: Protein, amino acid, vitamin B, C
- Therapeutic Actions: It nourishes lung, liver, stomach, spleen and blood. It clears heat, calms nerves, stimulates appetite and transforms phlegm. It can restrain the generation of many bacteria; it can also help to lower blood sugar. It is used for cancer, a decreased blood count, and chronic hepatitis.

Potato:
- Properties: Sweet, neutral
- Nutritional Contents: Starch, protein, vitamin B, C, lactic acid, and Citra conic acid
- Therapeutic Actions: Harmonizes stomach and adjusts vital energy, reinvigorates spleen and nourish qi, heals inflammation, stomach weakness, general fatigue and constipation.

Pumpkin:
- Properties: Sweet, cold
- Nutritional Contents: Calabshinine, adenine, carotene, vitamin B, C, amylaceum, saccharose
- Therapeutic Actions: Lubricates lung, replenishes vital energy and qi.

Radish:
- Properties: Pungent, slight cold, sweet
- Nutritional Contents: Amylaceum, vitamin B, C.
- Therapeutic Actions: Reinvigorates stomach to improve digestion, stops cough to resolve phlegm, soothes qi and improves urination, clears away heat and detoxifies body.

Snow Peas:
- Properties: Sweet, neutral
- Nutritional Contents: Protein, fat, sugar, calcium, iron, and phosphate
- Therapeutic Actions: Improves urination, stops diarrhea, adjusts vital energy and removes swellings. It can be used to treat hypertension and other heart diseases.

Scallions:
- Properties: Pungent, warm
- Nutritional Contents: Protein, fat, sugar, carotene, vitamin B1, B2, calcium, magnesium, iron
- Therapeutic Actions: Induces perspiration, removes coldness, phlegm and induces urination, improves digestion and whets appetite, excites nervous system and promotes blood circulation.

Spinach:
- Properties: Sweet, cold
- Nutritional Contents: Chlorophyll, iron, vitamins A, B, C, oxalic acid
- Therapeutic Actions: Cleans intestines, replenishes and activates blood, quenches thirst, lubricates lungs, adjusts vital energy and improves digestion. It is applied to hypertension, constipation and hemorrhoids.
- Caution: Not for cold stomach and loose bowels. Also, the oxalic acid reacts chemically with calcium, hampering the body from absorbing calcium. It is suggested that you not cook spinach with calcium-heavy food like beans, shrimp and sea tangle. If you insist you must do so, boil the spinach for 2 minutes beforehand to remove the oxalic acid.

Squash:
- Properties: Sweet, warm
- Nutritional Contents: Betacarotene (vitamin A), vitamin C
- Therapeutic Actions: It nourishes the spleen, stomach, yang and blood, promotes blood circulation and the healing of inflammation, and helps to relieve pain.

Chinese Yam:
- Properties: Sweet, neutral
- Nutritional Contents: Amylase, vitamins, mucus, starch, and amino acid
- Therapeutic Actions: It nourishes spleen and lungs, reinvigorates spleen to restrict seminal emission. It can be used for patients with persistent cough and asthma. And it is also used to treat involuntary and frequent sperm emission, night sweats, diarrhea, involuntary discharge of urine, frequent urination and abnormal female genital discharge.

Taro:
- Properties: Sweet, neutral
- Nutritional Contents: Vitamin B, C, starch, minerals, and lactic acid
- Therapeutic Actions: It nourishes stomach and spleen and is used to treat stomach diseases like ulcers and protracted constipation.

Tomato:
- Properties: Sour and slight sweet, neutral
- Nutritional Contents: Protein, fat, sugar, calcium, phosphate, iron, carotene, vitamin B1, B2 and C.
- Therapeutic Actions: Clears away heat and detoxifies, cools blood and calms the liver.

Towel Gourd
- Property: Sweet, neutral
- Nutrition Contents: Amino acids, sugar, vitamin B, C, fat, protein
- Therapeutic Action: It clears heat from blood, detoxifies, relaxes the muscles and stimulates the blood circulation, promotes the circulation of body fluid to remove swelling. It is used for productive cough, reduction of swelling, cardiovascular diseases, chronic respiratory system diseases, and milk deficiency in new mothers.

Turnip:
- Properties: Sweet, pungent and bitter, neutral
- Nutritional Contents: Vitamin C, phosphate, mustard oil and amylase
- Therapeutic Actions: It is a yang and blood tonic and helps blood circulation, clears interior heat, dries dampness, lowers rebellious nature, and can be used as diaphoretic to relieve water retention.
- Caution: Do not eat too much, especially with an empty stomach.

Water Chestnut:
- Properties: Sweet, slight cold
- Nutritional Contents: Vitamin B, fiber
- Therapeutic Actions: Clears away heat, resolves phlegm and lowers blood pressure. It can be used to treat hypertension and chronic cough.

White gourd:
- Properties: Sweet, slight cold
- Nutritional Contents: Oil, sugar, protein, vitamin B1, B2, niacin
- Therapeutic Actions: Dispels dampness to clear heat and quench thirst, improves urination to remove swelling, and relieves chest suppression. It contains low sodium and used to treat kidney diseases and edema.

Yellow Bean Sprouts:
- Properties: Sweet, cool
- Nutritional Contents: Protein, phosphate, calcium, and vitamin B1, B2, C
- Therapeutic Actions: It nourishes the spleen and stomach, clears blood vessel, removes swelling, reinvigorates the large intestine and reduces cholesterol. Good for diabetes and obesity.

GRAINS

Barley:
- Properties: Salty, warm and slightly cold
- Nutritional Contents: Malt sugar, amylaceum, vitamin B, amylase, lecithinum and dextrin
- Therapeutic Actions: Nourishes qi and adjusts vital energy, improves digestion, treats severe indigestion caused by excessive eating of improper foods and abdominal distension, promotes urination.

Millet:
- Property: Sweet, slightly cold
- Nutrition Constituent: Vitamin B1, B2, niacin, protein, fat, sugar
- Therapeutic Action: It harmonizes the stomach and calms restlessness. It is used to alleviate sleeplessness and weak digestion.

Wheat bran:
- Properties: Sweet, slight cold
- Nutritional Contents: Starch, protein, sugar, fat, and vitamin B
- Therapeutic Actions: Calms restlessness, alleviates sweat due to body deficiencies. It helps with night sweats and for those experiencing a burning thirst with resulting loss of sleep.

White rice:
- Properties: Sweet, neutral
- Nutritional Contents: Starch, protein, fat, vitamin B, and mineral salt
- Therapeutic Actions: Nourishes spleen and stomach.

LEGUMES

Black Soybean:
- Properties: Sweet, neutral
- Nutritional Contents: Fat, protein, sugar, vitamin B1, and niacin
- Therapeutic Actions: It adjusts vital energy and qi, promotes the circulation of body fluid to remove swelling and toxins. It is used for fever and night sweats due to fatigue after illness.
- Caution: Not for gout as it is high in protein.

Mung Beans:
- Properties: Sweet, cold
- Nutritional Contents: Starch, fat, protein, vitamin A, B2
- Therapeutic Actions: Promotes the passage of body fluid to remove swelling,

clears away heat and detoxifies. It is used for throat pain and constipation due to excess interior heat.

Red Beans:
- Properties: Sweet and sour, neutral
- Nutritional Contents: Starch, fat, protein, sugar, and vitamins A, B, C
- Therapeutic Actions: Clears away heat and improves urination, removes swelling and resolves extravagated blood.

Soybeans:
- Properties: Salty, cold
- Nutritional Contents: Protein, fat, iron.
- Therapeutic Actions: Nourishes large intestines, removes swelling, detoxifies, and lowers cholesterol.

Soy Sauce:
- Properties: Salty, cold
- Nutritional Contents: Protein, amino acid, fat, sugar, vitamin B1, B2, and niacin
- Therapeutic Actions: It helps to clear away heat and calms restlessness.

String Beans:
- Properties: Sweet, slight warm
- Nutritional Contents: Protein, fat, starch, vitamin A, B, C, calcium, phosphate, iron, niacin, and amino acid
- Therapeutic Actions: It helps to harmonize vital energy, reinvigorates stomach and clears away heat. It is used for stomach and spleen deficiencies due to interior heat such as stomach pain in summer, and diarrhea and vomiting due to vital energy disorder such as acute inflammation of the intestines.
- Caution: String beans have haemocylolysis and contain a kind of protein called agglutinant which are harmful. Cooking deeply is the only way to prevent them from harming the body.

Sword Beans:
- Properties: Sweet, neutral
- Nutrition Contents: Protein, fat, lecithinum
- Therapeutic Actions: It adjusts vital energy, nourishes kidney and stomach and stops vomiting.
- Caution: Not for gout as it is high in protein.

Tofu:
- Properties: Sweet, salty, cold, neutral
- Nutritional Contents: Protein, fat, sugar, niacin, vitamin B, and amino acid
- Therapeutic Actions: It helps to nourish yin, relieves dryness, harmonizes the stomach and qi, replenishes blood, removes blood stasis and promotes the production of milk and circulation of body fluids to remove swelling, clears away heat. It is a good food for cardiovascular diseases, diabetes and obesity

NUTS

Lotus Seed:
- Properties: Sweet, neutral
- Nutritional Contents: Starch, protein, fat, and vitamin C.
- Therapeutic Actions: One of the best foods for restoring vital energy. Strengthens spleen and arrests dysentery, restricts seminal emission. It is applied to palpitations and insomnia, fatigue and feelings of weakness, abnormal female genital discharge and chronic dysentery.

Sesame Seeds:
- Properties: Sweet, neutral
- Nutritional Contents: Oleic acid, sugar, lecithinum, and protein
- Therapeutic Actions: Lubricates intestines and harmonizes blood, nourishes liver and kidney, darkens hair. It is uses to alleviate fatigue due to kidney deficiency, premature white hair, anemia, insufficient body fluid, constipation, dizziness and tinnitus.

HERBS

Coriander:
- Properties: Pungent, warm
- Nutritional Contents: Fat oil, vitamins
- Therapeutic Actions: Removes rashes and promotes blood circulation, dispels coldness and wind, removes odor, and works as a lung and stomach tonic. It alleviates the symptoms of measles, and can remove the smell of meat when cooked with them. It detoxifies the body.

Dried Ginger:
- Properties: Hot, pungent
- Nutritional Contents: Starches, betabisabole, ginserols
- Therapeutic Actions: Works as a lung, stomach and spleen tonic, helps blood circulation, warms the interior and lubricates lungs to resolve phlegm. It helps stop a cough, removes toxins from the body, and stimulates the movement of the stomach to improve digestion and stops vomiting.

Ginger:
- Properties: Pungent, slightly warm
- Nutritional Contents: Pungent volatile oil, starches and resin.
- Therapeutic Actions: Induces sweat, warms the interior, stops vomiting and detoxifies the body. It is used for flu, cold spleen and stomach due to deficiencies. Can be used as diaphoretic to relieve water retention and detoxifies poisoning caused by fish and crab. It helps blood circulation, and alleviates the symptoms of fever and headache, and lessens phlegm and vomiting. Hot ginger soup removes coldness caused by a cold climate.

Garlic:
- Properties: Pungent, warm
- Nutritional Contents: Protein, fat, sugar, and vitamins A, B, C.
- Therapeutic Actions: Soothes qi, expels wind and coldness, detoxifies body, dispels worms, arrests loose bowels, improves urination, lowers blood pressure, arrests bleeding, removes phlegm, diminishes inflammation, reinvigorates the stomach, induces the production of stomach acid, lowers blood pressure and cholesterol, resolves extravagated blood. Eating raw garlic can protect you against bug bites.
- Caution: It creates "fire" or heat in the body, consumes blood and irritates eye vision. Not for those with stomach diseases. Eating garlic to excess can sometimes cause liver irratation.

Ginseng:
- Properties: Sweet and slight bitter, slight warm
- Nutrition Contents: Polysaccharides, ginsenosides, Rgl and Rbl
- Therapeutic Actions: It invigorates the primordial qi, nourishes spleen and lung, promotes the production of body fluid to quench thirst, and tranquilizes the mind. It is used for shortness of breath, mental fatigue, fainting and indistinct pulse due to severe or chronic illnesses, profuse bleeding and excessive vomiting or diarrhea, poor appetite, loose stool, fatigue due to kidney deficiency, and dyspnea and spontaneous perspiration due to deficiency of the lung and the kidney.
- Caution: Not for those with diseases resulting from interior heat.

FRUIT

Apple:
- Properties: Sour, neutral
- Nutritional Contents: Apple acid, dihydroxysuccinic acid, tannin, sugar, fat, vitamins A, B, C, fiber
- Therapeutic Actions: Nourishes heart and qi, promotes saliva to quench thirst, reinvigorates stomach and harmonizes spleen, stops diarrhea. It can be used for indigestion, light diarrhea and constipation.

Apricot:
- Properties: Sweet and sour, warm, very yang
- Nutritional Contents: Sugar, protein, calcium, phosphate, iron, vitamins A, B1, B2, and C
- Therapeutic Actions: Lubricates intestines and improves digestion.
- Caution: Do not overeat as the Chinese say, "Apricot hurts." It irritates teeth, stomach and intestines.

Chinese Red Date:
- Properties: Sweet, neutral
- Nutritional Contents: Protein, sugar, organic acid, and vitamin B, C
- Therapeutic Actions: Nourishes spleen and stomach, tonifies blood and relieves restlessness. Chinese call the date the "fruit of the spleen". It is mainly used for stomach and spleen deficiencies, anemia, peliosis, a decrease in blood platelets, and hepatitis. A very good nourishing food during the menstrual cycle and after giving birth.

Granada:
- Properties: Sweet, warm
- Nutritional Contents: Sugar, tannin
- Therapeutic Actions: An antibiotic can be used for dysentery, inflammation of the intestines, gallbladder and lung infections, lymphonditis, boils.

Grapes:
- Properties: Sweet, neutral
- Nutritional Contents: Sugar, protein, vitamin B1, B2, C, niacin and minerals.
- Therapeutic Actions: Replenishes vital energy, dispels wind and coldness and improves urination. It is used to dispel poor appetite due to fatigue and deficiencies.

Hawthorn Fruit:
- Properties: Sweet and sour, slight warm
- Nutritional Contents: Crataegin, tannin, fruit sugar, vitamin C, protein, fat oil
- Therapeutic Actions: Enhances the function of enzymes to improve digestion of meat, restrains the generation of epidemic dysentery. It can reduce blood pressure, dilate blood vessels and reduce cholesterol, is especially useful to control arteriosclerosis hypertension. It can help cure abdominal pain after delivery. Some people use it to treat an enlarged liver or spleen.

Peach:
- Properties: Sweet and sour, cool

- Nutritional Contents: Volatile oil, vitamin B
- Therapeutic Actions: Resolves extravagated blood, lubricates intestines and calms cough. It is used to treat painful menstruation, hypertension, blood vessel embolism, and traumatic injuries. Peach is called "the fruit of the lungs" in China, and is especially useful in treating lung diseases.

Pear:
- Properties: Sweet and slight sour, cold
- Nutritional Contents: Fructopyranose, amylaceum, organic acid, vitamin B, C, carotene, minerals
- Therapeutic Actions: Lubricates lungs to stop cough, resolves phlegm and clears interior heat, lowers blood pressure.
- Caution: Do not overeat as it induces dampness, which harms spleen and stomach.

Persimmon:
- Properties: Sweet, cold
- Nutritional Contents: Protein, fat, sugar, starch, tannic acid, vitamins and minerals
- Therapeutic Actions: Promotes the production of body fluids, lubricates lungs, astringes intestines and lowers blood pressure.
- Caution: Don't overeat and avoid eating on an empty stomach. Do not eat during recuperation after illness, after giving birth, or if you are anemic.

Tangerine:
- Properties: Sweet and sour, warm
- Nutritional Contents: Amylaceum, vitamin C
- Therapeutic Actions: Reinvigorates stomach, soothes qi, stops cough and resolves phlegm. Used for gas stagnation in stomach and spleen, indigestion, makes a productive cough. It is useful for treating some chronic cardiovascular diseases like hypertension, coronary disease and fever.

Watermelon:
- Properties: Sweet, cold
- Nutritional Contents: Orthophosphoric acid, apple acid, fructopyranose, amylaceum, amino acid, carotene, vitamin C
- Therapeutic Actions: Relieves chest congestion, thirst, throat ache, brown urine, canker sores and coughing up blood due to interior heat.
- Caution: Do not overeat, as it induces dampness and coldness.

MISCELLANEOUS FOODS

Brown sugar:
- Properties: Sweet, warm
- Nutritional Contents: Molasses, chlorophyll, xanthophyll, caroten and iron
- Therapeutic Actions: It warms interior, promotes the circulation of blood to remove stasis. Chinese women usually use brown sugar during the menstrual cycle and after giving birth. It can be used to treat stomach problems.

Honey:
- Property: Sweet, neutral
- Nutritional Constituent: Amylaceum, saccharose, dextrin, protein, minerals, wax, organic acid, enzyme, vitamins B1, B2, B6, C, E, niacin, potassium
- Therapeutic Actions: Restores deficiencies, moistens lungs, strengthens stomach and spleen, stops pain and detoxifies body. It can be used for abdominal pain due to spleen and stomach deficiencies, asthma, unproductive cough and constipation. Used to nourish the heart muscles and protect the liver, and lower blood pressure. It is used for cardiovascular diseases, anemia, gastro-duodenal ulcer, eye diseases, liver diseases and arthritis.

Tea:
- Properties: Sweet and bitter, slight cold
- Nutritional Contents: Vitamin A, B1, theanine, volatile oil, coffin
- Therapeutic Actions: Clears interior heat, sedates the mind, improves digestion, awakens nerves, improves urination, detoxifies the body, and lowers cholesterol. It can be used for inflammation of the intestines, arteriosclerosis and hypertension.
- Caution: Not for constipation and women in lactation period as it may restrict milk production.

Vinegar:
- Property: Sour and bitter, warm
- Nutritional Constituent: Ethylic acid, sugar, vitamins, aldehyde and salt
- Therapeutic Action: Strengthens stomach to improve digestion. The Ethylic acid in vinegar can kill bacteria or restrain them from growing, can be used for intestinal worms. Vinegar can prevent vitamin C loss and helps the absorption of calcium. It is also helpful in treating ringworm, diseases of the respiratory system, hypertension and arteriosclerosis.

Raw sugar:
- Properties: Sweet, cool
- Nutrition Contents: N/A
- Therapeutic Actions: It lubricates lung, clears away heat.

- Caution: Always use sugar in moderation. Sugar can cause many diseases to progress.

Wine:
- Properties: Sweet and pungent, warm-hot
- Nutrition Contents: N/A
- Therapeutic Actions: Moderate drinking can promote blood circulation and expel coldness from the body. In China, wines are widely used in medicine because they help the healing properties in herbs progress quickly.
- Caution: Drinking too much can severely harm your health.

PART TWO:
Chinese Recipes for Health

CHAPTER 5
Recipes for Health

Beverages

Almond Tea

Medicinal Uses:

Moistens lungs and eliminates congestion.

Improves digestion and relaxes the bowls.

Helps to prevent cancer, especially lung and intestinal.

Removes toxic material from the body.

Ingredients:

0.2 *ounces of sweet almonds*

0.35 *ounces of green tea*

Directions:

1. Wash the sweet almonds with cold water and then smash them into pieces.
2. Put the green tea into a cup.
3. Put almond pieces into a steel pot and cover with a half glass of water. Heat over a medium flame, bringing to a boil. Pour mixture over the green tea in the cup.
4. Cover cup and allow the tea to steep for five minutes before serving.

Note: Sweet almond is considered mild and nontoxic in nature and can be taken with tea regularly. Bitter almond has very little toxicity as well but should not be used every day.

Chrysanthemum Tea

Medicinal Uses:
Nourishes the liver
Improves vision.
Cools you when overheated.
Relieves gas and bloating.
Lowers blood pressure and promotes blood circulation.

Ingredients:

0.38   ounces of dried chrysanthemum

Directions:

1. Rinse the petals with cold water to remove any dirt.
2. Put petals into a cup and cover in boiling water. Cover and allow tea to steep for 5–10 minutes.
3. Refresh tea with more boiling water until the water begins to run clear.

Note: You should drink Chrysanthemum tea the same day it is made. It can't be left over night. The chrysanthemums that are grown in Anhui Province of China are the best. Those from Zhejiang and Henan also are of good quality.

Golden Corn-tassel Tea

Medicinal Uses:
Cools you when overheated.
Acts as a diuretic.
Relaxes the liver and induces gall.
Lowers blood pressure
Lowers blood sugar.

Ingredients:
1 *ounce of fresh corn tassel OR*
0.5 *ounces of dried corn tassel*

Directions:
1. Rinse the tassel with cold water.
2. Drain and cut the tassel and put in a cup.
3. Pour in boiling water and cover the cup.
4. Steep for 10 minutes.
5. Refresh tea with more boiling water until water runs clear.

Note: Fresh corn tassel works best for this drink. You can collect the fresh tassel from the corn and dry it in the sun. Then store the completely dried tassels in a sealed container.

Heart-healthy Hawthorn Juice

Medicinal Uses:
Refreshes the mind.
Improves the appetite.
Softens blood vessels.
Lowers blood pressure.

Ingredients:
0.2 *ounces of dried hawthorn slices*
1 *teaspoon of raw sugar*

Directions:
1. Put the hawthorn slice into a teapot and pour in boiling water.
2. Cover the pot and let mixture sit until cool.
3. Put sugar into a glass.
4. Poor hawthorn juice mixture into glass and stir well.

Sweet Dragon-eye Soup

Medicinal Uses:
  Improves appetite.
  Invigorates the spleen.
  Relaxes the mind.
  Enriches the blood.

Ingredients:
  10 *longans fruits*
   5 *dates*
   1 *teaspoon of brown sugar*

Directions:
  1. Remove the shells of the longans.
  2. Put longans and dates in a pot. Pour in 1 quart of water.
  3. Cover the pot and simmer for 15 minutes.
  4. Remove the pot from the heat.
  5. Pour in brown sugar and mix well.

Fresh Fruit Nectar

Medicinal Uses:
   Moistens the lungs and relieves cough.
   Eliminates congestion.
   Acts as a diuretic.
   Reduces fever.
   Lowers blood pressure.
   Especially effective for treating flu-related coughs.

Ingredients:

   1   apple
   1   pear
   1.8   ounces of sugar
   2–3   pieces of orange (or tangerine) peels
   1   quart of water

Directions:

1. Peel the apple and pear; remove their cores and cut into large cubes.
2. Add 1 quart of water into a pot.
3. Add orange peels, sugar, apple, and pear cubes.
4. Cover the pot and simmer for 30 minutes.
5. Allow to cool before drinking.

Olive Tea

Medicinal Uses:
Promotes the production of body fluids.
Reduces fever.
Improves the appetite.
Smoothes qi (energy).
Clears the throat and quenches thirst.

Ingredients:
5 or 6 olives
1 teaspoon of sugar

Directions:
1. Put clean olives, together with 1.5 quarts of water, into a pot. Cover and simmer over high heat till the olives begin to break down.
2. Remove the pot and filter to remove olive pieces.
3. Add sugar into the mixture and mix well.
4. Allow to cool down for drinking.

Orange-grove Tea

Medicinal Uses:
Smoothes qi.
Relieves cough and congestion.
Invigorates the stomach.
Reduces fever.
Enhances skin health.

Ingredients:
0.2 ounces of fresh orange or tangerine peels OR
0.4 ounces of dried orange or tangerine peels
1 teaspoon of sugar

Directions:
1. Clean the peels. Tear into small pieces and put into a teapot.
2. Pour boiling water into the pot, cover, and allow to steep for 5–10 minutes.
3. Pour into individual teacups and add sugar.

Pear Nectar Zing

Medicinal Uses:
Clears the lungs and relieves cough.
Eliminates congestion.
Removes heat from the body.

Ingredients:

2	*pears*
1	*teaspoon of white wine*
1	*teaspoon of sugar*
2 or 3	*pieces of orange peels*

Directions:

1. Peel the pears, leaving the stems on, and put them in a pot. Add sugar, orange peels, and 1 quart of water.
2. Simmer over medium heat for an hour.
3. Remove and discard pears.
4. Add wine into the mixture and stir well.
5. Allow to cool before drinking.

Forest-floor Pine-needle Tea

Medicinal Uses:
Relieves gas and bloating.
Removes dampness.
Removes obstructions in the channels.
Relieves arthritis pain.
Can prevent the flu and epidemic meningitis.

Ingredients:

0.35 ounces of fresh pine needles OR

0.18 ounces of dried needles

0.035 ounces of green tea

Directions:
1. Tear pine needles into small pieces and put in a cup together with 0.035 ounces of green tea.
2. Fill cup with boiling water, cover, and steep for about 5 minutes.
3. Refresh tea with more boiling water until the water runs clear.

Note: Pine needles collected in the cold winter months are the best. Dry them in the sun and store in a sealed container.

Perfectly Plum Juice

Medicinal Uses:
Prohibits intestinal bacteria and worms.
Prevents other diseases of the intestinal tract.

Ingredients:

2 or 3 plums

1 teaspoon of raw sugar

Directions:
1. Put 2 large bowls of water and plums into a pot.
2. Cover and simmer over medium heat until the plums turn into pulp.
3. Remove and discard the plums.
4. Add in raw sugar and stir until melted
5. Allow to cool and then drink.

Gingered Spinach

Medicinal Uses:
Relieves dehydration or dryness.
Helps with anemia.
Relieves hypertension
Eliminates hemorrhoids.

Ingredients:
- 8 *ounces of spinach*
- 1 *teaspoon of ginger juice*
- 2 *teaspoons of vinegar*
- 1 *stalk of green onion*
- 1 *teaspoon of salt*
- 1/2 *tablespoon of cornstarch*
- 2 *tablespoons of vegetable oil*
- 1/2 *tablespoon of sesame oil*

Directions:
1. Wash spinach and cut leaves in half down the middle.
2. Cut green onion into small chunks.
3. Make sauce by mixing ginger juice, vinegar, salt, and cornstarch into a cup of water.
4. Sprinkle sesame oil over the mixed sauce.
5. Heat vegetable oil in wok over high heat.
6. Put in green onion chunks and stir-fry for 15 seconds; then slide in spinach to cook for 5 minutes.
7. Pour the sauce over the spinach and stir-fry for 1 minute.
8. Transfer to a plate and serve.

Hot Brown-sugar Toddy

Medicinal Uses:
Warms energy channels.
Removes cold from the body.
Relieves restlessness and calms the mind.
Warms the stomach and eliminates dampness.
Relieves menstrual or gynecological problems due to cold intrusion and blood congestion.

Ingredients:
- *0.35 ounces of ginger*
- *7 whole white pepper corns*
- *3 teaspoons of brown sugar*

Directions:
1. Cut the ginger into thin slices.
2. Grind the white pepper.
3. Put brown sugar, ginger, and pepper into a steel pot.
4. Add half a bowl of water and simmer over low heat for 3 minutes.
5. Filter and serve while hot.

Note: During her menstrual cycle, a woman should drink a half a bowl one to two times a day.

Soups

Bamboo Shoots and Tofu Soup

Medicinal Uses:

Nourishes the blood
Removes heat from the body.
Detoxifies the body.
Balances the warm energy of meat.
Relieves chronic gastritis.
Fights cardiovascular diseases.
Good for women who have just given birth.

Ingredients:

3   *ounces of tofu*
1.5   *ounces of bamboo shoots*
1/2   *teaspoon of salt*
1/2   *teaspoon of pepper*

Directions:

1. Cut bamboo and tofu into thin slices.
2. Put 1/4 gallon of water in a wok over high heat till boiling.
3. Slide bamboo and tofu slices into the wok, cook for 5 minutes.
4. Add in salt and pepper to taste.
5. Mix well to serve.

Beef and Spinach Soup

Medicinal Uses:
Nourishes the stomach.
Promotes blood circulation and enriches blood.
Relieves dryness.
Relaxes the bowels.

Ingredients:

- 1.5 *ounces of beef*
- 5 *ounces of spinach*
- 1/2 *teaspoon of salt*
- 2 *teaspoons of sesame oil*

Directions:

1. Cut beef into 1-inch x 1-inch slices.
2. Wash spinach and put into boiling water for 30 seconds.
3. Remove and cut into 1.5-inch strips.
4. Bring 1/4 gallon of water to boil over high heat.
5. Add in beef slices and allow to cook for 5 minutes. Then add spinach strips and allow to cook for 2 more minutes.
6. Add in salt to taste.
7. Mix well and serve.

Crucian Carp and White-gourd Soup

Medicinal Uses:
  Promotes fluid passage to remove swelling.
  Nourishes the liver.
  Removes excess heat from the body.
  Harmonizes the stomach.
  Helps fight liver disease
  Treats abdominal swelling and edema.

Ingredients:
  1 *pound of crucian (or other suitable) carp*
  1 *pound of white gourd with peel*
  3 *tablespoons of vegetable oil*
  2 *tablespoons of cooking wine*
  1/2 *teaspoon of salt*
  1/2 *tablespoon of green-onion pieces*
  1/2 *tablespoon of ginger strips*

Directions:
  1. Clean fish, removing all internal organs except roe.
  2. Wash and drain.
  3. Remove seeds from white gourd.
  4. Wash and cut gourd into 1-inch cubes.
  5. Heat vegetable oil in wok over medium heat. Slide in green onion and ginger, followed by crucian.
  6. Cook fish on both sides until golden brown.
  7. Add cooking wine and salt.
  8. Continue to cook for 1 more minute.
  9. Pour in 1/3 gallon of cold water and bring to a boil.
  10. Transfer everything from the wok into a soup pot and add gourd cubes.
  11. Simmer over a low heat for 1 hour.
  12. Serve.

Delicious Dynasty Soup

Medicinal Uses:

Nourishes the stomach and spleen.
Is excellent for patients during a recovery period.
Treats fatigue due to kidney deficiency.
Treats hypertension.
Reduces high blood sugar.

Ingredients:

6 or 7 *pieces of dried shrimp*

2 *eggs*

1.8 *ounces of cooked chicken or pork*

0.8 *ounces of bamboo shoots*

1/2 *teaspoon of salt*

1/2 *tablespoon of sesame oil*

Directions:

1. Soak the dried shrimp in warm water for 10 minutes.
2. Cut cooked chicken or pork into thin strips.
3. Cut bamboo shoots into slices.
4. Beat and whip eggs in a small bowl.
5. Put 3 bowls of water into a pot and bring to a boil.
6. Add in chicken, shrimp, bamboo shoots, and salt.
7. Bring soup to a boil again. Pour whipped eggs into the pot while stirring quickly.
8. Remove from heat, sprinkle with sesame oil, and serve.

Tasty Shrimp and Turnip Soup

Medicinal Uses:
　Aids in the circulation of body fluids.
　Nourishes the kidney.
　Relieves pains in the knees and loins caused by kidney deficiency.
　Strengthens bones and muscles.

Ingredients:
　　1　*ounce of dried shrimp*
　　8　*ounces of turnips*
　　1　*teaspoon of salt*
　1/2　*teaspoon of pepper*

Directions:
　1. Wash dried shrimp.
　2. Wash turnips and cut into 2-inch thin strips.
　3. Put dried shrimp into boiling water and cook for 5 minutes.
　4. Drop in turnip strips and cook for 10 more minutes.
　5. Add in salt and pepper and cook 1 more minute, while stirring to mix well.
　6. Transfer the soup to a bowl, sprinkle sesame oil, and serve.

Fresh Lotus Leaves and Beef Soup

Medicinal Uses:
Invigorates the spleen and stomach.
Cleans the large intestine.
Restores vitality.
Treats prolapse of the rectum.

Ingredients:

4   *pieces of fresh lotus leaves*

3   *pounds of beef*

2   *tablespoons of vegetable oil*

1   *teaspoon of salt*

4   *tablespoons of cooking wine*

2   *pieces of star anise*

Directions:
1. Wash lotus leaves, pile them together, and place in the bottom of a pot.
2. Clean beef and cut into 1-inch cubes.
3. Heat vegetable oil in wok over high heat. Slide in beef cubes and stir-fry for 5 minutes.
4. Add in cooking wine; then cover the wok to simmer 10 minutes.
5. Transfer beef into the pot with lotus leaves.
6. Add in just enough water to immerse the beef.
7. Cook over medium heat till boiling.
8. Reduce to low heat and simmer for 2 hours.
9. Add in salt and star anise and continue simmering for another 1.5 hours, until the beef cubes become very tender.
10. Remove to serve.

Pork Spareribs With Kelp Soup

Medicinal Uses:

Nourishes blood and qi.

Clears up congestion and other obstructions.

Softens blood vessels.

Clears heat away form the body.

Helps to lower blood cholesterol.

Prevents fat accumulation.

Specifically used to treat arteriosclerosis, hypertension, diabetes, swollen glands, and edema.

Ingredients:

7   ounces of kelp

2   pounds of pork spareribs

1   tablespoon of vegetable oil

3   tablespoons of cooking wine

3/4   teaspoon of salt

Directions:

1. Soak kelp in cold water for 2 hours.
2. Rinse kelp and cut into thick strips.
3. Clean ribs and cut into cubes.
4. Heat vegetable oil over medium heat in wok and add ribs. Stir-fry for about 5 minutes.
5. Put in 2 tablespoon of cooking wine and a cup of water. Cover the wok and simmer for about 5 minutes.
6. Remove ribs and place into a soup pot.
7. Pour just enough water into the pot to immerse the ribs.
8. Bring to a boil and then add a spoon of cooking wine.
9. Reduce to low heat and simmer for 2 hours.
10. Add in salt and simmer for another 1/2 hour. allowing the ribs and kelp to become very tender.
11. Remove the pot from the heat and serve.

Gingered Lamb Soup

Medicinal Uses:
Replenishes blood to warm the body.
Adjusts menstruation to stop cramping and pelvic pain.
Used to treat coldness, stomach pain, and irregular menstruation caused by blood deficiency.

Ingredients:

2 *ounces of Angelica sinensis (Dong Quai)*
1/2 *ounce of ginger*
2 *pounds of lamb*
3 *tablespoons of vegetable oil*
1 *teaspoon of salt*
4 *teaspoons of cooking wine*
1 *dried tangerine peel*

Directions:

1. Rinse Angelica sinensis and drain.
2. Clean and cut ginger into thick slices.
3. Clean lamb and cut into 1-inch cubes.
4. Heat vegetable oil in wok over high heat. Slide in ginger and stir-fry for 10 seconds.
5. Add lamb cubes and stir-fry for 5 minutes.
6. Add in 2 teaspoons of cooking wine and cover wok, simmering for 5 minutes.
7. Transfer lamb cubes to a soup pot.
8. Add Angelica sinensis to pot and pour in just enough water to immerse the lamb.
9. Let mixture stand for 1/2 hour.
10. Bring to a boil over high heat.
11. Add in salt, remaining 2 teaspoons of wine, and dried tangerine peel.
12. Reduce to low heat and simmer for 2 hours.
13. Remove from heat and serve. (Discard Angelica sinensis before eating).

Kelp Egg Drop Soup

Medicinal Uses:

Nourishes blood and qi.

Clears congestion and other obstructions.

Helps to lower blood cholesterol and prevent fat accumulation.

Specifically used to treat arteriosclerosis, hypertension, swollen glands, and edema.

Ingredients:

1.5 *ounces soaked kelp*

2 *eggs*

1 *teaspoon green-onion chips*

1 *teaspoon coriander*

1 *tablespoon sesame oil*

2 *tablespoons soy sauce*

64 *ounces chicken or pork broth*

1/2 *teaspoon salt*

1 *tablespoon cooking wine*

1 *teaspoon pepper*

1/2 *lb cooked white rice*

Directions:

1. Cut kelp into 1/2-inch-wide and 2-inch-lomg strips.
2. Cut green-onion and coriander into 1-inch strips.
3. Beat and whip the egg.
4. Heat sesame oil in wok over medium heat; then slide in green-onion strips and stir-fry quickly for 10 seconds.
5. Add in soy sauce.
6. Pour chicken broth in and bring to a boil.
7. Add in kelp and salt.
8. Put cooked white rice into wok; then add in coriander strips. Bring to a boil and add in whipped egg, mixing well.
9. Sprinkle on cooking wine and pepper.
10. Remove from heat and serve.

Herbed Lamb Soup

Medicinal Uses:
Nourishes the spleen, kidney, and lungs.
Calms the liver.
Treats coldness.
Enhances immunities.
Specifically used to treat cancer and chronic fatigue.

Ingredients:

  2 *pounds of lamb spareribs*
  1 *teaspoon of ginger slices*
  2 *pieces of Chinese Angelica root (Dong Quai)*
  1 *piece of root*
  1 *piece of ginseng*
  1 *tablespoon of wolfberry fruit*
  10 *ounces of turnip*
  5 *pieces of Chinese red date*
  1 *teaspoon of salt*

Directions:
  1. Place lamb spareribs in a large soup pot and add 2 gallons of water.
  2. Bring water to a boil. Skim off surface of water.
  3. Add in the remaining ingredients.
  4. Reduce to low heat and simmer for 4 hours.
  5. Remove from heat to serve.

Laver, Tofu, and Pork Soup

Medicinal Uses:

Clears away heat and moistens lungs.
Reduces blood pressure and cholesterol.
Clears up decongestion.
Used to treat hypertension, arteriosclerosis, thyroid-gland enlargement, and cough.
Cancer preventive.

Ingredients:

1/2 *ounce of laver (a sea vegetable)*
1 *ounce of pork*
6 *ounces of tofu*
1/2 *teaspoon of salt*
1 *tablespoon of cooking wine*
1/2 *tablespoon of starch*
1 *stalk of green-onion*

Directions:

1. Tear laver into pieces and put into a soup bowl.
2. Chop green onion into small pieces.
3. Wash pork and cut into thin slices; add 1/2 teaspoon salt, 1 tablespoon of cooking wine, and 1/2 tablespoon of starch and mix evenly.
4. Cut tofu into thick pieces.
5. Put 1/4 gallon of water in a wok over medium heat and bring to a boil. Slide tofu into boiling water and add remaining salt.
6. Bring to a boil over medium heat.
7. Put pork slices into pot and cook for another 5 minutes.
8. Sprinkle green-onion pieces and remove pot immediately from the heat.
9. Pour soup into the bowl with laver and serve.

Lily and Chinese Red-date Soup

Medicinal Uses:
Nourishes the spleen and stomach.
Promotes the production of fluid.
Harmonizes the lung's qi.
Enriches heart blood.
Treats coughs, especially in the fall.

Ingredients:

- 1 *ounce of fresh (or dried) lily*
- 10 *pieces of Chinese red dates*
- 1 *tablespoon of raw sugar*

Directions:

1. Wash fresh lily and drain. If using dried lily, soak it for 10 minutes before washing.
2. Soak dates in warm water for 5 minutes; wash and drain.
3. Put lily, dates, and sugar together into a soup pot with 3 bowls of water.
4. Simmer over low heat for an hour.
5. Remove and serve.

Sweet Red-bean Soup

Medicinal Uses:

Removes heat from the body.

Removes toxic material from the body.

Enriches the blood.

Calms the mind.

Lifts qi.

Lowers blood pressure.

Acts as a diuretic.

Relieves swelling.

Ingredients:

9   ounces of red beans

10   dates

1   teaspoon of brown sugar

Directions:

1. Put the cleaned red beans into a pot.
2. Add 1.5 quarts of water.
3. Cover the pot and simmer for 40 minutes.
4. When red beans have opened up, add dates.
5. Cover and simmer for another 15–20 minutes.
6. Remove the pot and mix in brown sugar.

Mung Bean Soup

Medicinal Uses:
Cleans the gallbladder.
Nourishes the stomach.
Moistens the throat.
Clears away body heat.
Quenches thirst.
Used to treat chronic cholecystitis.

Ingredients:
- 2 *ounces of mung bean*
- 2 *tablespoons of raw sugar*

Directions:
1. Wash mung beans and put into a soup pot; then pour in 1/4 gallon of cold water.
2. Simmer over medium heat for half an hour.
3. Add in raw sugar.
4. Reduce to low heat and simmer for another half-hour, until the beans soften.
5. Remove pot and serve.

Mushroom and Snow Peas Soup

Medicinal Uses:
Nourishes skin.
Replenishes protein.
Lowers cholesterol.
Used to treat hypertension and diabetes.

Ingredients:

2 *ounces of dried mushrooms*

1 *ounce of snow peas*

1 *tablespoon of olive oil*

1/2 *teaspoon of salt*

1 *teaspoon of soy sauce*

1.5 *tablespoons of starch*

1/2 *tablespoon of ginger slices*

Directions:

1. Soak dried mushrooms in 1/2 gallon warm water for 15 minutes. Remove the mushrooms. Filter water to remove sediment and dirt.
2. Put mushrooms and water into a pot; combine snow peas, olive oil, salt, soy sauce, starch, and ginger.
3. Cover the pot and cook over medium heat for 10 minutes.
4. Transfer to a serving bowl.

Pork and Green-bean-sprout Soup

Medicinal Uses:
Clears away heat from the body.
Quenches thirst.
Induces milk production for new mothers.
Helps to reduce high postpartum blood pressure.

Ingredients:

2   *ounces of pork*
1   *cup of green-bean sprouts*
1/2   *tablespoon of green-onion pieces*
1/2   *tablespoon of starch*
1   *tablespoon of olive oil*
1   *tablespoon of cooking wine*
1/2   *teaspoon of salt*

Directions:

1. Wash and slice pork into thin strips.
2. Combine with salt, cooking wine, and starch. Mix evenly.
3. Wash and drain green-bean sprouts. Let stand.
4. Heat olive oil in wok over high heat.
5. Add in sprouts and stir-fry for 1 minute.
6. Pour in a large bowl of water. Bring to a boil and add pork strips.
7. Simmer for 5 minutes.
8. Sprinkle with green-onion pieces and serve.

Ribs, Peanuts, and Lotus-root Soup

Medicinal Uses:

Nourishes the stomach and blood.

Invigorates the stomach and spleen.

Improves joint flexibility.

Promotes milk production.

Used to treat chronic stomach diseases like gastritis, gastroduodenal ulcer, and ptosis of the stomach, as well as anemia, intestinal bleeding, and osteoporosis.

Ingredients:

   1   *pound of pork ribs*

   1   *lotus root*

   1   *ounce of peanuts*

 0.8 *ounces of ginger*

   2   *stalks of green-onion*

   1   *teaspoon of salt*

Directions:

1. Chop the ribs into small pieces.
2. Cut lotus root into 1-inch-thick chunks.
3. Cut the ginger into big slices.
4. Cut each green-onion stalk into 4 parts
5. Fill the pot 3/4ths of the way with cold water.
6. Add ribs to water and bring to a boil. Skim water surface.
7. Reduce to low heat and add peanuts, lotus-root chunks, ginger, onion, and salt.
8. Simmer for about 40 minutes over low heat, until food is tender.
9. Remove and serve.

Sweet and Sour Tomato Juice

Medicinal Uses:

Helps create body fluid.

Increases the appetite.

Harmonizes blood vessels and reduces blood pressure.

Clears away heat and toxic materials from the body.

Helps to stop capillary bleeding.

Used to treat cardiovascular disease in the summer.

Ingredients:

2   *tomatoes*

1   *tablespoon of honey*

Directions:

1. Wash tomatoes with cold water; then cut into thick pieces and place into a bowl.
2. Add honey to the bowl and coat tomato pieces evenly.
3. Cover the bowl and let stand for 1–2 hours, until most of the tomato juice comes out.
4. Serve.

Sour Noodle Soup

Medicinal Uses:

Promotes the production of body fluid.
Nourishes the stomach and spleen.
Clears away interior heat.
Used to treat flu, cardiovascular diseases, and obesity.

Ingredients:

1	*pound of Chinese noodles*
1/2	*pound of young Chinese cabbage*
2	*tablespoons of vinegar*
1	*tablespoon of soy sauce*
2	*ounces of tofu*
1/2	*teaspoon of salt*
1/2	*tablespoon of green-onion chips*

Directions:

1. Cut tofu into 1/2-inch cubes and cabbage into 1-inch strips.
2. Cook noodles in boiling water according to package directions
3. Add tofu cubes and cabbage strips to noodles and bring to a boil.
4. Remove food from water and then mix with salt, vinegar, and soy sauce.
5. Serve.

Soybean and Pork Spareribs Soup

Medicinal Uses:

Helps to enrich blood and nourish the liver.
Strengthens bones and kidneys.
Replenishes qi.
Reduces swelling and edema.
Used to treat hypertension, diabetes, edema, and anemia.

Ingredients:

1   *pound of soybeans*
2   *pounds of pork spareribs*
1   *teaspoon of salt*
2   *tablespoons of vegetable oil*
2   *tablespoons of cooking wine*
2   *stalks of green onion*

Directions:

1. Soak soybeans in water for 1 hour, drain, and let stand.
2. Cut green onion into 1-inch pieces, using only the white of the onion.
3. Wash spareribs and cut into 2-inch pieces.
4. Heat vegetable oil in wok over high heat.
5. Slide in green onion and stir-fry for 5 minutes.
6. Add 1 tablespoon of cooking wine and salt.
7. Cover the wok and simmer for 8 minutes.
8. Transfer ribs and soybeans into a soup pot.
9. Pour just enough water into the pot so that the solids are immersed.
10. Cook over high heat until the water boils.
11. Add remaining cooking wine; then reduce to low heat and simmer for nearly 3 hours.
12. Remove pot when soybeans and ribs are soft.

Spinach and Pork Soup

Medicinal Uses:

Nourishes the stomach.
Promotes blood circulation.
Used to treat hypertension.
Purges pathogenic heat and enriches the blood.
Relieves dryness.
Relaxes the bowels.
Helps fight cancer.

Ingredients:

8	*ounces of spinach*
2.5	*ounces of pork*
1	*teaspoon of salt*
1	*tablespoon of cooking wine*
1/2	*tablespoon of starch*
1/4	*tablespoon of olive oil*
1/4	*gallon water (chicken or pork broth can be used)*

Directions:

1. Remove all yellow leaves and root hairs from fresh spinach; then wash and drain.
2. Slice pork into thin strips.
3. Combine 1/2 teaspoon of salt, 1 tablespoon cooking wine, and 1/2 tablespoon of starch and mix well in a bowl.
4. Put 1/4 gallon of water (even better if chicken or pork broth is used) in a wok over medium heat to boil.
5. Put in remaining salt and 1 tablespoon of olive oil; then slide in pork strips and cook for 3 minutes.
6. Add spinach and cook for another 3 minutes.
7. Remove to serve.

Sticky-rice Soup

Medicinal Uses:
Warms the interior.
Enriches blood and adjusts qi.
Nourishes skin.
Used to treat abnormal menstruation.

Ingredients:

- 7 *ounces of sticky rice*
- 5 *ounces of lotus seeds*
- 12 *pieces of Chinese red date*
- 2 *tablespoons of brown sugar*

Directions:

1. Place ingredients in a pot with 1/2 gallon of water.
2. Bring to a boil over high heat.
3. Reduce to low heat and simmer for 1 hour, until the lotus seeds and sticky rice appears to have "melted."

Tomato and Pork Soup

Medicinal Uses:

Promotes the production of body fluid.
Removes obstructions in blood vessels.
Nourishes the liver and spleen.
Promotes digestion.
Helps to prevent hypertension.
Used to treat chronic liver or gallbladder diseases.
Useful for treating cancer.

Ingredients:

4   tomatoes
3   ounces of pork
1   tablespoon of vegetable oil
1   teaspoon of salt
1   tablespoon of cooking wine
1/2   tablespoon of starch
1   stalk of green onion
3   cups of water

Directions:

1. Wash and cut tomatoes into thick slices.
2. Chop green onion into small pieces.
3. Cut pork into thin slices and mix well with salt, vegetable oil, and starch.
4. Heat vegetable oil in a wok over high heat. Slide tomato slices into wok and stir-fry for 2 minutes.
5. Pour 3 cups of water into wok and bring to a boil.
6. Add pork and continue boiling for another 5 minutes.
7. Sprinkle in green-onion pieces and serve.

Towel Gourd With Pork Soup

Medicinal Uses:
Clears away heat and cools the blood.
Removes congestion.
Promotes the circulation of body fluid.
Used to treat cardiovascular disease, chronic respiratory-system disease,
diabetes, and milk deficiency in women.

Ingredients:

2	*towel gourds*
2	*ounces of pork*
1/2	*pound of tofu*
1	*teaspoon of salt*
1/2	*tablespoon of starch*
1	*stalk of green onion*
1	*tablespoon of cooking wine*
32	*ounces of water*

Directions:

1. Scrape off gourd peel, wash, and cut into cubes.
2. Cut green onion into small pieces.
3. Wash pork and cut into thin slices.
4. Combine 1/2 teaspoon of salt, 1 tablespoon of cooking wine, and 1/2 table-spoon of starch in a bowl and mix evenly.
5. Cut tofu into half-inch cubes.
6. Pour 32 ounces of water into a wok and bring to a boil over medium heat.
7. Slide in pork slices, tofu cubes, and remaining salt.
8. Cook until the mixture boils again; then add in towel gourd and continue cooking for another 3 minutes. (Do not let the gourd turn yellow).
9. Sprinkle green-onion pieces on top and serve.

Spiced Turnip and Lamb Soup

Medicinal Uses:
   Nourishes spleen and stomach.
   Warms lungs and clears up congestion.
   Restores vitality and fights coldness.
   Used to treat tuberculosis.
   Useful in treating obesity.

Ingredients:

   2   *pounds of lamb*
   1   *pound of turnip*
   2   *ounces of carrot*
   2   *pieces of dried orange peels*
   3   *pieces of ginger slices*
   3   *tablespoons of vegetable oil*
   1   *teaspoon of salt*
   2   *tablespoons of cooking wine*

Directions:

1. Wash lamb and cut into 2-inch cubes, drain, and let stand.
2. Clean turnip and carrot; then cut into 2-inch cubes.
3. Heat vegetable oil in wok over high heat.
4. Add in ginger slices and stir-fry several minutes.
5. Slide in lamb cubes and stir-fry for 5 minutes.
6. Pour cooking wine into the wok and stir-fry for another 3 minutes.
7. Pour a half-bowl of cold water into the wok and simmer for 10 minutes.
8. Remove the lamb and carrots and put together with dried orange peels into a big soup pot.
9. Add just enough cold water so that the lamb is immersed.
10. Bring to a boil over medium heat and then add remaining cooking wine and salt.
11. Reduce to low heat and simmer for half an hour.
12. Add turnip cubes to the pot and simmer for another hour.
13. When lamb and turnips turn become soft, remove the pot from the heat and serve.

Water Chestnut With Lotus-root Soup

Medicinal Uses:
Clears away heat and toxic material.
Arrests bleeding.
Quenches thirst.
Clears up blood in the urine.
Useful for treating obesity.

Ingredients:

1   *pound of fresh water chestnut*
3   *ounces of fresh lotus root*

Directions:

1. Remove hairs from water chestnut's peel. Wash and drain.
2. Cut chestnuts into halves.
3. Wash lotus roots and cut each in two.
4. Put water chestnuts and lotus roots into a big soup pot.
5. Pour in three large bowls of water.
6. Simmer over low heat for half an hour.

Young Chinese Cabbage and Tofu Soup

Medicinal Uses:
Nourishes the stomach and intestines.
Clears away heat from the body.
Removes blood coagulation.
Helps to lower blood pressure and cholesterol.
Useful in treating diabetes.

Ingredients:

3   ounces of young Chinese cabbage
8   ounces of tofu
1   teaspoon of salt
1/2   tablespoon of sesame oil
1/4   gallon of water

Directions:

1. Pull yellow leaves and roots off the cabbage.
2. Wash, drain, and cut diagonally into two parts.
3. Cut tofu into thick pieces.
4. Pour 1/4 gallon of water into a wok over medium heat.
5. Bring water to a boil and slide in tofu. Salt to taste.
6. Bring to a boil again and add in the cabbage.
7. Cook for another 5 minutes and then remove wok from heat.
8. Sprinkle a little sesame oil into soup and serve.

Young Chinese Cabbage With Pig Liver Soup

Medicinal Uses:
Invigorates the liver and the gallbladder.
Clears intestines.
Nourishes the stomach.
Fights cancer growth (high in vitamin A)
Used to treat liver diseases.

Ingredients:

7	*ounces of young Chinese cabbage*
5	*ounces of pig liver*
1	*tablespoon of olive oil*
1	*teaspoon of salt*
2	*tablespoon of cooking wine*
1	*tablespoon of cornstarch*
32	*ounces of water*

Directions:
1. Clean cabbage. Soak in water for 5 minutes and rinse.
3. Clean and rinse liver.
4. Cut liver into thin slices and combine with salt, cooking wine, and cornstarch. Mix well.
5. Pour 32 ounces of water into a wok over high heat.
6. Bring to a boil and slide in cabbage, olive oil, and salt.
7. When it boils again, add in liver slices and cook for 2 minutes.
8. Remove and serve.

Note: Since pig liver is high in cholesterol, those with hypertension or cardiovascular disease should not eat this dish.

Meat Dishes

Beef With Bamboo Shoots

Medicinal Uses:
Nourishes blood.
Clears interior heat from the body.
Can be used to detoxify (bamboo is often used to balance the warm energy of meat.)
Nourishes the spleen and the stomach.
Replenishes blood.
Strengthens bones and muscles.

Ingredients:
- 1/2   *pound of beef*
- 3   *ounces of bamboo shoots*
- 2   *stalks of green onion*
- 1/2   *tablespoon of ginger chips*
- 1/3   *tablespoon of sugar*
- 1/2   *tablespoon of pepper*
- 1   *tablespoon of soy sauce*
- 2   *tablespoons of cooking wine*
- 1   *tablespoon of sesame oil*
- 1/2   *teaspoon of salt*
- 4   *tablespoons of vegetable oil*
- 1   *tablespoon of starch*
- 1 1/2   *cups of water*

Directions:
1. Cut beef into matching strips.
2. Combine beef with starch and cooking wine. Mix well.
3. Cut green onions (using only the white sections) and bamboo shoots into matching strips.
4. Melt remaining starch in 1/2 cup of water.
5. Heat 2 spoons of vegetable oil in wok over high heat.
6. Slide in beef strips and stir-fry for 1 minute. Remove from wok and let stand.
7. Heat remaining oil and slide in bamboo shoot, green onion, and ginger; stir-fry for 20 seconds.

8. Pour soy sauce, cooking wine, sugar, and 1 cup of water into wok.
9. Slide in beef strips and stir-fry 1 minute; then add in pepper, sesame oil, and salt. Mix well.
10. Transfer to a plate and serve.

Beef With Chestnuts

Medicinal Uses:

Nourishes the spleen and kidney.
Strengthens muscles and bones.
Replenishes qi and blood.
Used to treat softness of the waist and knee and urine frequency due to kidney deficiency.
Treats the effects of spleen and stomach weakness.

Ingredients:

1.5 *pounds of beef*
10 *ounces of chestnuts*
1 *teaspoon of ginger chips*
1 *teaspoon of green-onion chips*
2 *tablespoons of soy sauce*
1/4 *tablespoon of pepper*
1/2 *teaspoon of salt*
2 *tablespoons of cooking wine*
2 *tablespoons of vegetable oil*

Directions:

1. Wash beef and boil for 30 minutes.
2. Remove beef and cut into 3-inch x 1-inch pieces.
3. Cut ginger into thin slices and green onion into 2-inch strips.
4. Cut a notch on each chestnut; then put them into boiling water for 10 minutes to soften and remove shells.
5. Heat vegetable oil in wok over high heat. Put in chestnuts and beef separately to stir-fry until browned.
6. Remove and drain oil in the wok. Let chestnuts and beef stand separately.
7. Put green-onion strips and ginger slices into wok and stir-fry for 10 seconds; then put the beef back in along with salt, pepper, cooking wine, and 1 1/2 cups of water.

8. Bring to a boil and remove bubbles on the surface. Reduce heat and simmer 20 minutes.
9. Add chestnuts and simmer for another 15 minutes.
10. Remove and serve.

Ginger Beef

Medicinal Uses:
Nourishes the spleen and the stomach.
Replenishes blood.
Strengthens bones and muscles.

Ingredients:
1 *pound of beef*
7 *ounces of ginger*
3 *tablespoons of vegetable oil*
1 *teaspoon of salt*

Directions:
1. Shave ginger and cut into pieces.
2. Cut beef into 1-inch x 1-inch slices.
3. Make sauce by mixing cooking wine, and salt.
4. Heat 2 tablespoons of vegetable oil in wok over high heat.
5. Slide in beef slices and stir-fry for 3 minutes.
6. Remove and drain oil from beef.
7. Heat remaining oil, slide in ginger pieces, and stir-fry for 1 minute; then pour in the sauce.
8. When the sauce boils, slide in beef slices and stir-fry for another 2 minutes.
9. Remove and serve.

Note: Ginger can be irritating if you have a cough or are congested.

Seared Beef With Turnip

Medicinal Uses:
 Nourishes spleen and stomach.
 Strengthens muscles and bones.
 Promotes blood circulation.
 Useful for treating hypertension and diabetes.

Ingredients:
 1.1 *pounds of turnip*
 8.8 *ounces of lean beef*
 4 *tablespoons of vegetable oil*
 2 *tablespoons of cooking wine*
 4 *tablespoons of water*
 1/2 *teaspoon of salt*
 1/2 *tablespoon of soy sauce*
 1/2 *tablespoon of starch*
 1 *stalk of green onion*

Directions:
 1. Wash and peel turnips; then slice them into thin strips.
 2. Wash beef, slice, and cut into thin strips.
 3. Combine with 1/4 teaspoon of salt, 1 tablespoon of cooking wine, 1/2 table-spoon soy sauce and starch. Mix evenly and let stand.
 4. Heat 1 tablespoon of vegetable oil over high heat; then slide turnip strips into wok and stir-fry for 1 minute.
 5. Add remaining salt. Remove from wok and let stand.
 6. Heat remaining 3 tablespoons of vegetable oil over high heat; then slide in beef strips and cook for 3 minutes.
 7. Slide in turnip strips and stir; then add remaining tablespoon of cooking wine and 4 tablespoons of water.
 8. Simmer for 5 minutes; then sprinkle in green-onion pieces and mix well.
 9. Remove and serve.

Bitter Melon With Minced Pork

Medicinal Uses:　　　　

Clears away interior heat from the body.
Removes toxins.
Lowers blood sugar.
Serves as an ideal food for treating diabetes, hypertension, and high cholesterol.

Ingredients:

1　*pound of bitter melon*
3　*ounces of minced pork*
1　*tablespoon of soy sauce*
1　*tablespoon of cooking wine*
1　*teaspoon of salt*
1/2　*tablespoon of sugar*
2　*tablespoons of vegetable oil*
1/2　*tablespoon of green-onion chips*
1/2　*tablespoon of ginger chips*

Directions:

1. Wash bitter melon, cut it in half vertically, and remove the seeds; then cut the melon into thick slices.
2. Heat vegetable oil in wok over high heat; then slide in minced pork and stir-fry for 3 minutes.
3. Add in ginger, green onion, soy sauce, and cooking wine and stir for 30 seconds.
4. Slide in bitter melon and stir-fry for 3 minutes.
5. Add in salt and sugar. Mix well.
6. Remove and serve.

Egg With Pork Strips

Medicinal Uses:
Used to treat fatigue.
Reverses poor appetite due to hyperfunction of the spleen.
Helps combat weakness and thirst during convalescence.
Treats dry cough.
Nourishes the blood.

Ingredients:

  6   *ounces of lean pork*
  2   *eggs*
1/2   *teaspoon of salt*
  1   *tablespoon of starch*
  2   *tablespoons of vegetable oil*
1/2   *cup of water*

Directions:
1. Slice pork into thin 2-inch strips.
2. Combine salt, starch, and 1/2 cup of water. Mix well and set aside.
3. Beat and whip eggs; then pour over pork strips and mix evenly.
4. Heat vegetable oil over high heat, add all other ingredients, and stir-fry for 5 minutes.
5. Remove and serve.

Note: Since egg yolk is high in cholesterol, those with heart disease should avoid this dish.

Fresh Snow Peas With Pork

Medicinal Uses:

Provides energy.
Nourishes the spleen and stomach.
Clears away excess heat from the body.
Used to treat hypertension and diabetes.

Ingredients:

- 5 *ounces of fresh snow peas*
- 3 *ounces of lean pork*
- 2 *tablespoons of cooking wine*
- 1/3 *teaspoon of salt*
- 1/2 *tablespoon of starch*
- 2 *tablespoons of vegetable oil*
- 2 1/2 *cup water*

Directions:

1. Cut lean pork into short, thin slices.
2. Combine half of the salt, 2 tablespoons of cooking wine, 1/2 cup of water, and starch. Mix well and let stand.
3. Boil snow peas in water for 6 minutes. Drain and let stand.
4. Heat vegetable oil in wok over high heat. Put in pork slices and stir-fry for 3 minutes.
5. Add 2 cups of water, then add the snow peas and remaining salt and cook for another 5 minutes.
6. Remove and serve.

Lamb Strips With Onion

Medicinal Uses:

Replenishes blood to warm the body.

Stops painful menstruation.

Used to treat coldness, stomach pain, and irregular menstruation due to blood deficiency.

Ingredients:

- 1/2 *pound of lamb*
- 5 *ounces of onion*
- 2 *tablespoons of soy sauce*
- 1 *tablespoon of sugar*
- 1/2 *teaspoon of salt*
- 2 *teaspoons of starch*
- 3 *tablespoons of vegetable oil*
- 2 *tablespoons of cooking wine*
- 1 *cup of water*

Directions:

1. Wash and cut lamb and onion into matching strips.
2. Melt starch in 1/2 cup of water.
3. Heat vegetable oil in wok over high heat. Slide in lamb strips and stir-fry for 1 minute.
4. Slide in onion strips and stir-fry for 3 minutes.
5. Add in cooking wine, soy sauce, sugar, and remaining 1/2 cup of water. Continue stir-frying for 2 minutes.
6. Pour in melted starch. Stir for 30 seconds to mix well with onion and lamb.
7. Remove and serve.

Note: Onion can create intestinal gas in people who are sensitive.

Lamb With Carrots

Medicinal Uses:

Warms stomach and restores deficiency.

Relieves gas and bloating.

Removes coldness.

Replenishes vital energy.

Invigorates yang and enriches the blood.

Used to treat gastric ulcers, hypertension, heart disease, and rheumatic arthritis.

Ingredients:

2.2 *pounds of lamb*

1.1 *pounds of carrots*

1 *tangerine peel*

5 *slices of ginger*

1 *teaspoon of salt*

4 *tablespoons of cooking wine*

1 *tablespoon of soy sauce*

3 *tablespoons of vegetable oil*

4 1/2 *cups of water*

Directions:

1. Clean lamb and cut into cubes.
2. Wash carrots and cut into cubes.
3. Dry-fry (without oil) carrots in a wok for 8 minutes; then transfer to a bowl and let stand.
4. Heat vegetable oil over high heat.
5. Slide in ginger slices then lamb and stir-fry for 5 minutes.
6. Add 3 tablespoons of cooking wine and cook for another 7 minutes.
7. Add salt, soy sauce, and 2 tablespoons of cold water and simmer for 10 minutes.
8. Transfer everything into a soup pot; then add the carrots and tangerine peel.
9. Pour in 4 1/2 cups of water and simmer over high heat.
10. Add remaining tablespoon of cooking wine, reduce heat, and continue simmering for 2 hours, until lamb cubes turn soft.
11. Remove and serve.

Lamb With Cucumber

Medicinal Uses:

Replenishes blood to warm the body.

Treats painful menstruation.

Used to treat feelings of body coldness, stomach pain, and irregular menstruation due to blood deficiency.

Relieves symptoms of hypertension and diabetes.

Ingredients:

- 3 ounces of lamb
- 5 ounces of cucumber
- 2 teaspoons of soy sauce
- 2 teaspoons of cooking wine
- 1/3 teaspoon of salt (divided in half)
- 1 teaspoon of green-onion chips
- 1/2 teaspoon of ginger chips
- 2 teaspoons of starch

Directions:

1. Cut lamb into 1-inch x 1-inch slices and place in a bowl.
2. Combine starch, 1 teaspoon of soy sauce, and cooking wine. Mix well.
3. Cut cucumber into 1-inch x 1-inch pieces. Combine with 1/2 the salt and mix well.
4. Heat vegetable oil in wok over high heat; then slide in lamb slices and stir-fry for 3 minutes.
5. Slide in green onion, ginger chips, and cucumber pieces and stir-fry for 3 minutes.
6. Add in remaining salt and soy sauce and stir several times to mix well.
7. Transfer to a dish and serve.

Leek With Bacon in Black-bean Sauce

Medicinal Uses:
  Assists in the cure of blood-vessel-related diseases.

Ingredients:
  3 *ounces of leek*
  1 *tablespoon of black-bean sauce*
  7 *ounces of bacon*
  1/4 *teaspoon of salt*
  1/2 *teaspoon of sugar*
  1 *tablespoon of vegetable oil*

Directions:
  1. Wash and cut leek into 1-inch strips
  2. Cut bacon into thin slices.
  3. Heat vegetable oil in wok over high heat; then add bacon and black-bean sauce and stir-fry for 3 minutes.
  4. Add leek, salt, and sugar to the wok and continue stir-frying for another 5 minutes.
  5. Transfer to a dish and serve.

Lotus Root With Pork

Medicinal Uses:
  Nourishes the blood.
  Used to treat anemia and bleeding.

Ingredients:
  5   *ounces of lean pork*
  8   *ounces of lotus roots*
  1/2   *teaspoon of salt (divided in half)*
  1   *tablespoon of soy sauce*
  1   *tablespoon of starch*
  2   *tablespoons of vegetable oil*
  1   *cup of water*

Directions:
  1. Cut the pork into thin slices and combine with half the salt, a cup of water, and starch.
  2. Shave the lotus roots and cut into thin slices.
  3. Make sauce by mixing soy sauce and remaining salt.
  4. Heat vegetable oil over high heat and push in pork slices to stir-fry for 3 minutes.
  5. Put in lotus-root slices to stir-fry for 5 minutes. Pour the sauce (from step 3) over and mix well. Cook 1 minute.
  6. Serve.

Marbled Pork With Chives

Medicinal Uses:
Treats impotence and premature ejaculation.
Reduces frequent urination and knee pain caused by a kidney deficiency.
Improves digestion.

Ingredients:

1/2	*pound of marbled pork*
2	*ounces of chives*
1	*tablespoon of vegetable oil*
1/2	*tablespoon of cooking wine*
1/2	*tablespoon of raw sugar*
1/2	*tablespoon of soy sauce*
1/4	*teaspoon of salt*

Directions:
1. Wash pork and cut into thin strips.
2. Wash chives, drain, and cut into 1-inch pieces.
3. Heat 1 tablespoon of vegetable oil in wok over high heat; then slide in pork strips and stir-fry for 1 minute.
4. Add chives and stir-fry 30 more seconds.
5. Pour in cooking wine, soy sauce, and sugar. Stir to mix well.
6. Transfer and serve.

Pork and Eggs

Medicinal Uses:
Treats restlessness and wakefulness.
Reduces excessive heat in the hands and feet.
Removes an unproductive cough as it lubricates dryness. Replenishes the blood.
Invigorates the spleen.
Used to treat women after giving birth to replenish blood and calcium.

Ingredients:
- 0.7 *ounces of lean pork*
- 2 *eggs*
- 1 *teaspoon of green-onion pieces*
- 2 *tablespoons of vegetable oil*
- 3 *pieces of ginger slices*
- 1/4 *teaspoon of salt*
- 1/2 *tablespoon of cooking wine*
- 4 *tablespoons of water*

Directions:
1. Cut pork into 1-inch strips.
2. Break eggs and whip.
3. Heat 1 tablespoon of vegetable oil in wok over medium heat.
4. Stir-fry eggs for 2 minutes. Remove and let stand.
5. Heat remaining vegetable oil in wok over high heat; then slide in green-onion strips and pork strips.
6. Stir-fry for 3 minutes; then add in soy sauce, cooking wine, ginger, salt, and egg.
7. Add 4 tablespoons of water and continue stir-frying for 5 minutes.
8. Transfer and serve.

Pork and Spinach

Medicinal Uses:

Nourishes the stomach.
Promotes blood circulation.
Purges the body of excessive heat.
Enriches the blood.
Relieves dryness in the body.
Relaxes the bowels.
Helps prevent cancer.

Ingredients:

1   *pound of spinach*
3   *ounces of pork*
2   *stalks of coriander*
1   *carrot*
1   *tablespoon of vegetable oil*
1/2   *tablespoon of soy sauce*
1/2   *tablespoon of vinegar*
1/3   *teaspoon of garlic chips*
1/2   *teaspoon of salt*
1/4   *tablespoon of pepper*

Directions:

1. Wash spinach and quickly boil in hot water for 30 seconds. Remove and drain.
2. Cut into three sections and put them on a plate.
3. Cut carrot into thin strips and boil quickly in hot water for 30 seconds. Remove, drain, and place on bed of spinach.
4. Cut coriander into chips and place on spinach.
5. Slice pork into thin strips.
6. Heat vegetable oil in wok over high heat and slide in pork strips.
7. Add pepper and soy sauce and stir-fry quickly for 1 minute.
8. Pour pork strips together with sauce over spinach.
9. Add vinegar, salt, and garlic chips.
10. Stir to mix evenly and serve.

Pan-seared Pork Liver With Turnip

Medicinal Uses:
Fights cancer.
Improves vision.
Relieves swelling due to a liver deficiency.
Clears excessive heat from the body.
Improves digestion.
Promotes fluid passage, thus helping to cure hepatitis and chronic cholecystitis.

Ingredients:
- 8.8 *ounces of pork liver*
- 8.8 *ounces of turnip*
- 2 *tablespoons of cooking oil*
- 1/2 *teaspoon of salt (divided in half)*
- 1 *tablespoon of cooking wine*
- 1/3 *tablespoon of starch*
- 1 *teaspoon of green-onion pieces*

Directions:
1. Clean the pork liver and chop into thin slices.
2. Combine with 1/2 the salt, cooking wine, and starch. Mix evenly.
3. Wash turnip and cut into thin slices.
4. Heat 1 tablespoon of cooking oil in wok over high heat; then slide in turnip slices and stir-fry for 4 minutes while adding remaining salt. Remove from wok and let stand.
5. Heat another tablespoon of oil over high heat; then slide in liver slices and stir-fry for 3 minutes.
6. Slide in turnip slices again and continue stir-frying for another 3 minutes.
7. Remove, sprinkle green-onion pieces, and serve.

Spicy Pork Strips With Squash

Medicinal Uses:

Clears away excessive interior heat.
Cools the blood.
Promotes the circulation of body fluids.
Used to treat edema, hypertension, diabetes, and constipation.

Ingredients:

1	*pound of squash*
1	*ounce of pork*
1/3	*ounce of hot green pepper*
3	*tablespoons of vegetable oil*
1/2	*teaspoon of salt*
1	*tablespoon of starch*
2	*cloves of garlic*
1/2	*cup of water*

Directions:

1. Wash and cut pork into 1-inch strips, combine starch and 1/2 cup of water, and mix well.
2. Wash squash and cut into 1-inch x 1-inch pieces. Cut hot green pepper into 1/2 -inch ring sections. Crush garlic with knife.
3. Heat vegetable oil in wok over high heat. Put in garlic first and then the pork strips to stir-fry for 1 minute.
4. Put in squash pieces and green pepper. Stir-fry for 3 additional minutes.
5. Transfer and serve.

Pork With Celery and Dried Bean Curd

Medicinal Uses:
Restores deficiency.
Improves vision.
Promotes blood circulation while reducing blood pressure.

Ingredients:
- 3 stalks of celery
- 5.3 ounces of lean pork
- 1/2 pound of dried bean curd
- 3 tablespoons of vegetable oil
- 1/2 teaspoon of salt (divided in half)
- 1/2 tablespoon of cooking wine
- 2 tablespoons of water

Directions:
1. Remove celery roots and leaves. Wash and cut stalks into half-inch stems.
2. Wash pork and cut into thin strips.
3. Wash dried bean curd and cut into thin slices.
4. Heat 1 tablespoon of vegetable oil over medium heat; then slide in celery and stir-fry for 2 minutes.
5. Add 1/2 the salt; then transfer to a bowl and let stand.
6. Heat remaining 2 tablespoons of vegetable oil over medium heat; then slide in pork strips and cook for 2 minutes.
7. Slide in bean-curd slices; then add remaining salt and 2 tablespoons of water. Simmer for 3 minutes.
8. Slide in celery and continue stir-frying for 5 minutes.
9. Transfer and serve.

Tofu With Minced Pork

Medicinal Uses:

Relieves dryness.

Nourishes yin energy to reinvigorate vital energy.

Helps in milk production.

Harmonizes the liver and the spleen.

Used to treat chronic liver disease, hypertension, and diabetes.

Ingredients:

10 *ounces of tofu*

3 *ounces of minced pork*

1/2 *teaspoon of salt*

2 *teaspoons of soy sauce*

2 *teaspoons of cooking wine*

1 *teaspoon of sugar*

1/2 *tablespoon of green-onion chips*

1/2 *tablespoon of ginger chips*

1/3 *tablespoon of garlic chips*

1 *tablespoon of cornstarch*

2 *tablespoons of vegetable oil*

Directions:

1. Cut tofu into half-inch cubes and immerse in boiling water for 1 minute.
2. Heat vegetable oil in wok over high heat; then slide in minced pork and stir-fry for 3 minutes.
3. Add in ginger, green onion, and garlic, together with cooking wine, salt, and soy sauce. Stir-fry for 30 seconds.
4. Pour in 2 ounces of water and then add the sugar.
5. When water boils, slide in tofu cubes and cook for 2 minutes.
6. Sprinkle in cornstarch. Stir quickly for 1 minute until it evenly coats tofu cubes.
7. Transfer and serve.

Pork Strips With Celery and Carrot

Medicinal Uses:
Rebalances the intestines and stomach.
Lubricates the lungs.
Used to treat bronchitis, coughs, hypertension, obesity and diabetes.

Ingredients:

1   *stalk of celery*

3   *ounces of carrots*

2   *ounces of lean pork*

1   *tablespoon of starch*

1/2   *teaspoon of salt*

2   *tablespoons of vegetable oil*

1/2   *cup of water*

Directions:

1. Wash pork and cut into 1-inch strips.
2. Combine starch and a half-cup of water. Mix well.
3. Wash celery and carrots; then cut into matching strips.
4. Heat vegetable oil in wok over high heat; then slide in carrot strips and stir-fry for 3 minutes.
5. Slide in celery strips and pork strips and stir-fry for 3 minutes.
6. Add salt and mix well.
7. Transfer and serve.

Pork With Asparagus Lettuce

Medicinal Uses: ✳

Replenishes vital energy.
Invigorates the spleen.
Promotes the production of body fluids.
Induces milk production.
Used for lactating women and to treat diabetes.

Ingredients:

1   *pound of asparagus lettuce*

8.8   *ounces of lean pork*

2   *tablespoons of vegetable oil*

1/2   *teaspoon of salt (divided in half)*

1   *tablespoon of cooking wine*

1/2   *tablespoon of starch*

1/2   *tablespoon of green-onion pieces*

Directions:

1. Clean and cut asparagus lettuce into strips.
2. Wash and slice pork.
3. Combine with 1/2 of the salt, cooking wine, and starch. Mix well.
4. Heat 1 tablespoon of vegetable oil in a wok over high heat; then slide in asparagus lettuce and stir-fry for 3 minutes.
5. Add remaining salt and continue stir-frying for 3 minutes.
6. Transfer asparagus lettuce into a bowl and let stand.
7. Heat remaining vegetable oil over high heat. Slide in green onion followed by pork slices and stir-fry quickly for 3 minutes.
8. Slide in asparagus lettuce and continue stir-frying for 5 minutes.
9. Transfer and serve.

Pork With Carrots

Medicinal Uses:

Reinforces and replenishes vital energy.
Reduces blood pressure.
Improves vision.
Serves as a cancer preventive.

Ingredients:

8.8 *ounces of carrot*

3.5 *ounces of lean pork*

3 *tablespoons of vegetable oil*

1/2 *teaspoon of salt (divided in half)*

1 *tablespoon of cooking wine (divided in half)*

1 *stalk of green onion*

2 *tablespoons of water*

Directions:

1. Wash carrots and cut into thin slices.
2. Wash and cut pork into slices; then mix with 1/2 of the salt and 1/2 table-spoon of cooking wine. Let stand.
3. Heat wok over high heat; then slide in carrots and dry-fry for 10 minutes. Transfer to a bowl and let stand.
4. Heat vegetable oil over high heat; then slide in pork slices and stir-fry for 3 minutes.
5. Slide in carrots, add remaining salt and remaining cooking wine, and stir-fry for 1 minute.
6. Add 2 tablespoons of water and simmer for 2 minutes. Repeat this step 3 more times.
7. Sprinkle on green-onion pieces.
8. Transfer and serve.

Pork With Chestnuts

Medicinal Uses:

Nourishes the stomach and invigorates the spleen.

Nourishes yin energy.

Moistens dryness.

Used to treat symptoms of spleen deficiency.

Treats cough caused by overheated lungs.

Ingredients:

1/2 *pound of chestnuts*

1.5 *pounds of lean pork*

1/2 *teaspoon of ginger chips*

1 *teaspoon of green-onion chips*

1 *tablespoon of soy sauce*

8 *ounces of vegetable oil*

1/2 *teaspoon of salt*

1/2 *tablespoon of raw sugar*

Directions:

1. Cut a notch on each chestnut and put them in boiling water for 10 minutes to soften. Remove shells and inner skins.
2. Cut ginger into thin slices and green onion into 1-inch strips.
3. Wash pork and cut into 2-inch cubes.
4. Heat 8 ounces of vegetable oil over high heat; then slide in chestnuts and stir-fry for 3 minutes.
5. Remove and drain oil; then transfer chestnuts to a plate and let stand.
6. Remove excess oil, keeping only 1.5 ounces in the wok over medium heat.
7. Slide in ginger, green onion, and pork and stir-fry for 10 minutes.
8. Add 2 bowls of water and bring to a boil.
9. Remove residue from the surface of the water. Reduce heat and allow to simmer for 15 minutes.
10. Add chestnuts, salt, sugar, and soy sauce and continue simmering for 15 minutes.
11. Transfer and serve.

Pork With Coriander

Medicinal Uses:
Used to combat fatigue.
Treats poor appetite due to hyperfunctioning of the spleen.
Used to combat weakness and thirst during convalescence.
Relieves dry cough due to dryness of the lungs.

Ingredients:

3   *ounces of fresh coriander*

6   *ounces of lean pork*

1/2   *teaspoon of salt*

1/2   *tablespoon of starch*

2   *tablespoons of vegetable oil*

4   *tablespoons of water*

Directions:

1. Wash coriander and cut into 1-inch strips.
2. Cut pork into 1-inch thin strips.
3. Combine 1/4 teaspoon of salt, starch, and 4 tablespoons of water. Mix well.
4. Heat vegetable oil in wok over high heat; then slide in pork strips and stir-fry for 2 minutes.
5. Add in coriander strips and remaining salt and continue stir-frying for 3 minutes.
6. Transfer and serve.

Sautéed Lamb

Medicinal Uses:

Warms the interior energy channels.
Replenishes blood.
Warms the kidney to restore vitality.
Used to relieve vomiting, weakness, fatigue, and edema.
After giving birth, women use it to treat stomachache, weakness, and loin pain.
Used to treat impotence.
Counteracts cold phobia due to kidney deficiency.
Useful for treating diabetes.

Ingredients:

2   pounds of lamb
2   tablespoons of cooking oil
1/2   tablespoon of cooking wine
2   teaspoons of soy sauce
2   tablespoons of fennel
1   teaspoon of ginger slices
1/2   teaspoon of garlic chips
1   teaspoon of sugar
1   piece of hawthorn
5   tablespoons of water

Directions:

1. Wash lamb, first with cold and then with boiling water.
2. Cut lamb into half-inch cubes.
3. Heat oil in wok over high heat; then slide in lamb cubes together with wine, ginger slice, and fennel strips. Stir-fry for 10 minutes.
4. Add 5 tablespoons of water and the hawthorn. Continue to stir-fry for another 5 minutes.
5. Add in soy sauce and sugar and continue stir-frying for 20 minutes.
6. Add garlic pieces.
7. Transfer and serve.

Stewed Leg of Lamb

Medicinal Uses:
Warms up the spleen, stomach, and kidney.
Strengthens the urinary bladder.
Used to treat seniors who suffer from urinary frequency.

Ingredients:

8	*ounces of carrots*
3	*pounds of lamb leg*
3	*tablespoons of vegetable oil*
3	*tablespoons of cooking wine*
1	*teaspoon of salt*
2	*tablespoons of soy sauce*
1/2	*teaspoon of ginger slices*
1/2	*tablespoon of cassia barks*
	(available in Chinese grocery store)
1	*cup of cold water*

Directions:

1. Clean and cut lamb leg into 1-inch cubes.
2. Wash carrots and cut into 1-inch pieces.
3. Dry-fry (no oil) carrot cubes for 10 minutes; then transfer to a bowl and let stand.
4. Heat vegetable oil in wok over medium heat; then slide in ginger followed by lamb cubes and stir-fry for 5 minutes.
5. Add in cooking wine and stir-fry for another 5 minutes.
6. Add in salt, soy sauce, and 1 cup of cold water. Cover the wok and simmer for 10 minutes.
7. Transfer lamb cubes to a soup pot; then add in carrot cubes and cassia bark.
8. Pour in just enough cold water to immerse the lamb cubes.
9. Bring to a boil over high heat; then reduce heat and allow to stew for 2 hours.
10. Transfer and serve.

Stewed Lean Pork With Mushrooms

Medicinal Uses: ✳

Relieves abdominal distension or pain due to contradiction between liver and spleen.

Used to treat chronic hepatitis and diabetes.

Ingredients:

6 *ounces of lean pork*

2 *ounces of mushrooms*

1/2 *teaspoon of salt*

1 *stalk of green onion*

3 *ginger slices*

Directions:

1. Cut pork into half-inch cubes.
2. Put pork cubes in a soup pot; then pour in just enough water to immerse them.
3. Bring to a boil over high heat; then add in mushrooms, salt, ginger, and green onion.
4. Reduce heat and simmer for 45 minutes to allow pork cubes to become tender.
5. Transfer and serve.

Tofu With Beef

Medicinal Uses:
Nourishes the spleen and stomach.
Harmonizes the stomach.
Clears away toxins.
Replenishes protein.
Balances cholesterol.
Useful for treating heart disease.

Ingredients:

1.1	*pounds of tofu*
0.35	*ounces of beef*
2	*tablespoons of vegetable oil*
1	*tablespoon of snow peas*
1/4	*teaspoon of salt*
1/2	*tablespoon of starch*
1/2	*tablespoon of raw sugar*
1/4	*tablespoon of minced garlic*
1/2	*teaspoon of green-onion pieces*
1/2	*tablespoon of soy sauce*
1 1/2	*cups of water*

Directions:
1. Cut beef into tiny cubes.
2. Cut tofu into half-inch cubes.
3. Put Tofu in boiling water for 20 seconds. Remove and let stand.
4. Heat vegetable oil in wok over high heat; then slide in beef and stir-fry for 1 minute.
5. Add soy sauce, sugar, and 1 1/2 cups of water. Reduce to low heat and simmer for 10 minutes.
6. Add tofu and salt and stir several times; then continue to let simmer for 5 minutes.
7. Add snow peas and starch.
8. Sprinkle in garlic and green onion.
9. Transfer and serve.

Gammon, White Gourd and Mushroom

Medicinal Uses:

Nourishes the spleen and liver.

Improves the appetite.

Improves fluid passage.

Nourishes the kidney and promotes the production of body fluids.

Used to treat liver disease.

Helps to prevent cancer.

Ingredients:

2.1 *ounces of gammon*

0.5 *ounces of dried mushroom*

1.1 *pounds of white gourd*

1 *tablespoon of cooking wine*

1/2 *tablespoon of scallion (the white part)*

1/2 *teaspoon of salt*

Directions:

1. Wash gammon and cut into long slices.
2. Wash and drain dried mushrooms.
3. Wash and cut white gourd into cubes. Put them on a large plate, add the salt, and mix evenly.
4. Put gammon slices on white-gourd cubes and place mushrooms around them.
5. Sprinkle on cooking wine and scallion whites.
6. Put the plate in a large pot and add water, but not enough to float the plate.
7. Steam over high heat for 1 hour.
8. Carefully remove the plate and serve.

Poultry
Dishes

Spicy Gingered Chicken

Medicinal Uses:
Provides essential proteins and vitamins.
Aids in weight loss.
Used to treat hypertension and diabetes.

Ingredients:

> 3 *ounces of white chicken meat*
> 3 *ounces of hot green pepper*
> 2 *tablespoons of cooking wine*
> 1/2 *teaspoon of salt (divided in half)*
> 1/2 *teaspoon of pepper*
> 2 *tablespoons of starch*
> 1/2 *tablespoon of green-onion chips*
> 1/2 *tablespoon of thin ginger strips*
> 1/2 *teaspoon of garlic chips*
> 3 *tablespoons of vegetable oil*
> 1/2 *cup of water*

Directions:

1. Cut chicken into half-inch cubes.
2. Combine chicken with 1 tablespoon of cooking wine, a half-cup of water, half of the salt, and 1 tablespoon of starch. Mix well and let stand.
3. Slice hot green peppers into rings.
4. Make sauce by mixing remaining cooking wine, remaining salt, pepper, and starch.
5. Heat oil in wok over high heat; then slide in chicken cubes and stir-fry for 3 minutes.
6. Slide in hot green peppers, ginger, green onion, and garlic and stir-fry for another 8 minutes.
7. Sprinkle on sauce and continue stir-frying for 3 minutes.
8. Transfer and serve.

Chicken With Walnuts

Medicinal Uses:
Invigorates the lungs and kidney.
Improves vision.
Used to treat coughing and gasping due to deficiencies in the lungs and kidney.
Reduces dizziness due to anemia.
Relieves seniors' chronic inflammation and infection of the trachea.

Ingredients:
1/2 pound of white chicken meat
1/2 ounce of walnuts
1 teaspoon of Chinese wolfberry fruits (available in any Chinese grocery store)
2 eggs
1/2 teaspoon of salt (divided in half)
2 tablespoons of cooking wine
1/2 teaspoon of pepper
1/2 teaspoon of ginger chips
1/2 tablespoon of green-onion chips
1 tablespoon of sesame oil
1 tablespoon of raw sugar
2 tablespoons of starch
2 tablespoons of olive oil

Directions:
1. Soak walnut kernels in warm water until swelling. Remove skin.
2. Wash wolfberry fruit.
3. Cut ginger into thin slices and green onion into small pieces.
4. Remove and discard egg yolk and beat egg white.
5. Cut chicken into half-inch cubes.
6. Put chicken cubes in a bowl. Add half of the salt, the beaten egg white, and starch. Mix well.
7. Heat olive oil in wok over high heat; then slide in walnut kernels and stir-fry until the mixture turns egg-yellow. Transfer and let stand.

123

8. Slide chicken cubes into wok and stir-fry quickly for 1 minute.
9. Add in green onion and ginger together with sugar and pepper and stir-fry for 3 minutes.
10. Add in walnut kernels and wolfberry fruit and continue stir-frying for another 3 minutes. Add remaining salt. Mix well.
11. Remove, sprinkle on sesame oil, and serve.

Steamed Chicken With Chestnuts

Medicinal Uses:
Nourishes the spleen and stomach.
Invigorates the kidney
Strengthens the waist and feet.
Used to relieve chronic gastritis, kidney deficiency, and urinary frequency.
Used to treat waist and leg pains experienced by seniors.

Ingredients:

2.2 *pounds of fresh chestnuts*

1 *chicken (or game hen)*

3/4 *teaspoon of salt*

2 *tablespoons of cooking wine*

Directions:
1. Cut a notch in the middle of each chestnut and boil for 3 minutes. Drain, remove shells, and let stand.
2. Wash the chicken and cut into 1-inch cubes.
3. Mix chestnuts with chicken cubes. Put them in a basin, sprinkle with salt, and add
   cooking wine.
4. Put the basin in a large steamer and steam for 3 hours.
5. Transfer and serve.

Steamed Duck With Ginseng

Medicinal Uses:
   Invigorates and nourishes lung energy and the spleen.
   Enriches blood to strengthen the heart.
   Improves metabolism.
   Used to treat bronchitis, bronchiectasis, and tuberculosis.

Ingredients:

   1/2 *ounce of ginseng*
    1   *duck*
    2   *tablespoons of cooking wine*
   1/2 *tablespoon of salt*
    6   *ounces of water*

Directions:
1. Rinse the ginger and place in a small bowl.
2. Place the bowl in a pot with water and steam until soft.
3. Cut ginger into thin slices and let stand.
4. Wash the duck; then place it chest-up in a deep bowl.
5. Insert ginseng slices in its belly; then bend the duck head into the belly and sprinkle 1.5 tablespoons of cooking wine inside.
6. Sew duck belly up with thread.
7. Add 6 ounces of water; then add salt and remaining wine into the bowl. Cover the bowl to keep water vapor out.
8. Place the basin in a large steamer,* and steam for 4 hours until duck becomes tender.
9. Transfer and serve.

Note: Do not use red ginseng for this dish.

*A metal or bamboo steamer can be purchased in most oriental grocery stores as well as some mainstream cooking supply stores.

Stewed Duck With Garlic

Medicinal Uses:

Helps to promote vital energy and circulation of body fluids.

Removes swelling and coagulation.

It is used to treat food stagnation, as well as edema and chronic kidney disorders.

Aids in weight loss.

Helps to prevent cancer.

Ingredients:

   1   *duck*

   2   *ounces of garlic*

   1   *teaspoon of ginger slices*

   1   *stalk of green onion*

   3   *tablespoons of cooking wine*

   1/4   *tablespoon of pepper*

   1/2   *tablespoon of salt*

10 1/2   *cups water*

Directions:

1. Completely clean the duck, removing all internal organs and its feet.
2. Cut ginger into large pieces.
3. Peel the garlic and insert into duck's belly.
4. Put 10 1/2 cups of water in a large soup pot.
5. Put duck, ginger, salt, green onion, cooking wine, and pepper into the pot.
6. Bring to a boil over a high heat.
7. Skim residue from the surface.
8. Reduce heat and simmer for 1 hour.
9. Remove and serve

Seafood
Dishes

Shrimp With Steamed Egg

Medicinal Uses:

Replenishes protein.
Improves the appetite.
Used to treat chronic fatigue resulting from a kidney deficiency.
Useful for treating diabetes.

Ingredients:

0.35 *ounces of soaked, dried shrimp*

2 *eggs*

0.35 *ounces of snow peas*

0.35 *ounces of mushroom*

0.35 *ounces of potato*

0.35 *ounces of ham*

1/2 *tablespoon of starch*

1/2 *tablespoon of sesame oil*

1/2 *teaspoon of salt*

4 *cups of water*

Directions:

1. Beat eggs evenly in a bowl.
2. Place bowl in a pot with water and steam for 15 minutes.
3. Remove bowl and cut cooked egg into small cubes.
4. Cut potato, mushroom, and ham into small cubes.
5. Put 4 cups of water in wok over high heat; add dried shrimp, egg cubes, snow peas, potato cubes, mushroom cubes, and salt.
6. When mixture boils again, add the starch.
7. Transfer to a soup bowl.
8. Sprinkle in ham cubes and sesame oil and serve.

Squid With Pork and Chive Strips

Medicinal Uses:
Nourishes the stomach and spleen.
Stimulates the appetite.
Replenishes the body's vital essence.
Used to treat lung diseases and constipation.
Reverses weariness in the loins and knees due to kidney deficiency.

Ingredients:
- 7 *ounces of squid*
- 3.5 *ounces of pork*
- 4 *tablespoons of vegetable oil*
- 3.5 *ounces of chives*
- 2 *tablespoons of cooking wine*
- 1/2 *teaspoon of salt (divided in half)*
- 1 *tablespoon of sugar*
- 1 *teaspoon of vinegar*
- 1/2 *teaspoon of pepper*
- 2 *eggs*
- 2 *tablespoons of starch*

Directions:
1. Clean the squid and cut into 1.5-inch strips.
2. Cut chives and pork into 1-inch strips.
3. Remove egg yolk and beat egg white.
4. Put pork strips in a bowl and combine with half of the salt, the cooking wine, egg white, and starch. Mix well.
5. Make sauce by mixing soy sauce, sugar, remaining salt, vinegar, and pepper.
6. Heat 2 tablespoons of vegetable oil in wok over high heat; then slide in pork strips and stir-fry for 2 minutes.
7. Remove and let stand.
8. Heat another 2 tablespoons of oil, slide in squid strips, and stir-fry for 1 minute.
9. Slide in pork strips and chive strips and continue stir-frying for 4 minutes.
10. Pour in sauce and mix well.
11. Transfer and serve.

Sautéed Eel

Medicinal Uses:

Replenishes vital energy
Fights fatigue.
Removes dampness and gas in the body.
Promotes blood circulation
Reduces blood-sugar levels.
Used to treat rheumatic arthritis.

Ingredients:

1   *pound fresh eel*

3   *tablespoons of vegetable oil*

2   *tablespoons of cooking wine*

3   *teaspoons of soy sauce*

1   *teaspoon of garlic pieces*

1/2   *tablespoon of green-onion pieces*

1/4   *teaspoon of salt*

Directions:

1. Remove internal organs from eel, clean, and cut into 1-inch strips. Drain and let stand.
2. Heat oil in a wok over high heat; then slide in garlic pieces followed by eel strips and stir-fry for 3 minutes.
3. Add cooking wine. Cover the wok and simmer for 3 minutes.
4. Add in salt, soy sauce, and a bowl of cold water. Cover and simmer for another 25 minutes, until the eel strips turn soft.
5. Remove and sprinkle on green-onion pieces to serve.
6. Eat while hot.

Shrimp With Cauliflower

Medicinal Uses:

Reinvigorates the kidney and the stomach.

Treats weakness in the loins and knees due to kidney deficiency.

Helps to prevent cancer.

Ingredients:

8 *ounces of cauliflower*

2 *ounces of dried shrimp*

1/2 *teaspoon of salt*

4 *ounces of chicken soup*

1 *tablespoon of cornstarch*

1/2 *tablespoon of green-onion chips*

1/3 *tablespoon of ginger chips*

2 *tablespoons of vegetable oil*

1 *tablespoon of sesame oil*

1 *teaspoon of sugar*

Directions:

1. Cut cauliflower into small cubes and boil in water for 2 minutes.
2. Soak dried shrimp in boiling water for 10 minutes.
3. Heat vegetable oil in wok over high heat; then slide in cauliflower and stir-fry for 1 minute.
4. Add ginger chips, green onion, and chicken soup; then reduce to low heat, cover the wok, and simmer for 5 minutes.
5. Add salt and sugar.
6. Dissolve cornstarch in water and pour into the wok.
7. Slide in dried shrimp, sprinkle sesame oil, and stir.
8. Transfer and serve.

Shrimp in Tomato Sauce

Medicinal Uses:
  Stimulates the appetite.
  Promotes the production of body fluids.
  Nourishes the kidneys.
  Used to treat hypertension.
  Aids in weight loss.

Ingredients:

  8 *ounces of shrimp*
  3 *ounces of cucumber*
  1 *ounce of tomato sauce*
  2 *tablespoons of cooking wine*
  1/2 *teaspoon of salt (divided in half)*
  2 *teaspoons of vinegar*
  2 *teaspoons of sugar*
  1 *tablespoon of green-onion chips*
  1/2 *teaspoon of ginger chips*
  2.5 *ounces of vegetable oil*
  2 *tablespoons of cornstarch*
  1 *egg*
  1 *cup of water*

Directions:

1. Remove the dark thread on the backs of the shrimp (devein). Rinse and drain shrimp.
2. Combine half of the salt, 1.5 tablespoons of cooking wine, egg white, and 1 tablespoon of cornstarch. Mix well.
3. Halve cucumbers vertically and remove seeds. Then cut them into half-inch pieces.
4. Heat 1 ounce of vegetable oil in wok over high heat; then slide in shrimp and stir-fry for 3 minutes.
5. Transfer and let stand.
6. Pour remaining oil into the wok; then slide in ginger chips and green onion and stir-fry for 15 seconds.

7. Add in tomato sauce, remaining cooking wine, remaining salt, and a cup of water, followed by vinegar and sugar. Mix well to make sauce.
8. Thicken the sauce by adding remaining cornstarch.
9. Slide shrimp and cucumber pieces into the sauce and stir-fry for 5 minutes, until they are coated evenly with sauce.
10. Transfer and serve.

Salty Shrimp

Medicinal Uses
Used to treat pains in the loins and knees.
Useful in treating obesity.

Ingredients:

1	*pound of jumbo shrimp*
1/2	*teaspoon of salt*
1	*stalk of green onion*
1	*tablespoon of ginger slices*

Directions:
1. Clean and wash shrimp.
2. Cut green onion into 2-inch strips.
3. Put a gallon of water in wok over heat; then slide in peppers to boil for 5 minutes.
4. Remove and discard the peppers.
5. Slide in green-onion strips, ginger, and salt.
6. When water boils, add in shrimp, reduce to medium heat, and cook for 8 minutes.
7. Remove to serve.

Note: Since shrimp contains relatively high cholesterol, anyone with cholesterol problems should avoid all shrimp dishes.

Orange-flavored Shrimp

Medicinal Uses:

Clears excessive heat from the body.
Treats fevers and coughs.
Nourishes the stomach.
Stimulates the appetite.
Used to treat diabetes and stomach or kidney deficiencies.

Ingredients:

1	*pound of shrimp*
1	*ounce of tomato sauce*
1/2	*teaspoon of salt*
2	*tablespoons of cooking wine*
2	*teaspoons of vinegar*
2	*teaspoons of sugar*
1.7	*ounce of dried tangerine peels**
1/2	*tablespoon of ginger slices*
1	*tablespoon of green-onion chips*
1.2	*ounces of vegetable oil*

Directions:

1. Clean the shrimp and rinse.
2. Soak dried tangerine peels in warm water for 5 minutes.
3. Heat vegetable oil in wok over high heat; then stir-fry green onion and ginger for 15 seconds.
4. Slide in shrimp and stir-fry for 10 minutes, until they turn pink.
5. Add in tomato sauce, soaked tangerine peels, salt, cooking wine, sugar, vinegar, and 2 cups of water.
6. When it boils, reduce to low heat and simmer for 10 minutes.
7. Increase to high heat for 3 minutes to evaporate the sauce in the wok.
8. Discard tangerine peels, green onion, and ginger.
9. Transfer shrimp to a plate and serve.

*Tangerine peels can be purchased at any oriental market or you can dry your own.

Chives With Shrimp

Medicinal Uses:
Invigorates the kidney.
Reverses calcium depletion.
Treats osteoporosis.
Cleans the stomach and intestines to improve digestion.

Ingredients:
- 1/2 *ounce of dried shrimp*
- 1 *pound of chives*
- 3 *tablespoons of vegetable oil*
- 1/2 *teaspoon of salt*

Directions:
1. Wash chives and cut into 1-inch strips.
2. Place chive tips and leaves on separate plates.
3. Wash dried shrimp and drain completely.
4. Heat vegetable oil in wok over high heat; then slide in shrimp and stir-fry for 10 seconds.
5. Slide in chive tips and stir-fry for 3 minutes.
6. Add in chive leaves and stir-fry for 2 minutes.
7. Add in salt and mix well.
8. Transfer and serve.

Steamed Mandarin Fish With Garlic

Medicinal Uses:
Replenishes protein.
Nourishes the spleen and stomach.
Relieves fatigue due to hyperfunction of the spleen.
Used to treat tuberculosis patients.

Ingredients:

1 *pound of Mandarin fish*

4 *cloves of garlic (purple-peel garlic is preferred.)*

1/2 *teaspoon of salt*

2 *tablespoons of cooking wine*

Directions:

1. Scale fish to remove gills and internal organs. Rinse and drain.
2. Remove garlic peels. Insert one piece into fish mouth and put the rest into fish belly.
3. Put fish on a large plate. Sprinkle cooking wine and salt in and on the fish.
4. Place the plate in a steaming pot over high heat and steam for 40 minutes.
5. Transfer and serve.

Steamed Eel

Medicinal Uses:
Combats fatigue.
Balances various deficiencies in the body.
Treats deficiencies in calcium, protein, and phosphorus.
Regular intake can help tuberculosis patients to recover.
Fights wasting and weakness during convalescence.

Ingredients:
2 *pounds fresh eel*
1 *teaspoon of salt*
2 *tablespoons of cooking wine*
3 *pieces of sliced ginger*

Directions:
1. Clean eel, removing internal organs. Rinse and cut into 2-inch sections.
2. Put eel sections on a plate, sprinkle on salt and cooking wine, and place ginger slices on top.
3. Put the plate in a pot with water over high heat and steam for 1 hour.
4. Transfer and serve.

Butterfish With Garlic

Medicinal Uses:

Replenishes protein.
Acts as a tonic for the kidney and liver.
Improves vision.
Nourishes the brain.
Replenishes the spleen.
Improves the appetite.
Removes toxins.
Treats obesity, hypertension, indigestion, worms, edema, diabetes, and acute
and chronic epidemic diseases like dysentery, inflammation of the intestines,
typhoid fever, and flu.

Ingredients:

1   *pound of butterfish*
3   *ounces of garlic*
2   *tablespoons of soy sauce*
2   *tablespoons of cooking wine*
1   *tablespoon of vinegar*
1/2   *teaspoon of salt*
1   *teaspoon of sugar*
1   *tablespoon of chopped green onion*
1/2   *teaspoon of chopped ginger*
1/2   *teaspoon of chopped garlic*
1.5   *ounces of vegetable oil*
2   *cups of water*

Directions:

1. Scale the fish, remove its internal organs, and rinse completely.
2. Cut the fish diagonally on two sides. Each cut should be 1/3-inch deep.
   There are a total 4 cuts on each side, with a half-inch space between two
   cuts.
3. Paint the fish with 1 tablespoon of soy sauce, half of the salt, and 1 tablespoon of cooking wine. Let stand for 10 minutes.
4. Heat 1.5 ounces of vegetable oil in wok over high heat, then slide in fish
   and fry until it turns golden brown on both sides.
5. Remove and drain the fish. Transfer to a plate and let stand.
6. Leave about two tablespoons of vegetable oil in the wok over high heat.
   Add ginger, garlic, and green onion and stir-fry for 20 seconds.

7. Slide in fish, remaining soy sauce, remaining cooking wine, vinegar, remaining salt, sugar, and 2 cups of water.
8. Lower heat, cover wok, and simmer for 20 minutes.
9. Turn the fish over twice during simmering.
10. Transfer and serve.

Fried and Steamed Belt Fish

Medicinal Uses:
Replenishes protein.
Nourishes the kidney and brain.
Calms the liver.
Relieves chronic fatigue.
Used to treat loin and knee pain due to kidney deficiencies.

Ingredients:

1	*pound of belt fish*
2	*tablespoons of soy sauce*
1	*tablespoon of sesame oil*
5	*tablespoons of vegetable oil*
1/2	*teaspoon of salt*
1	*tablespoon of chopped green onion*
1/2	*tablespoon of ginger slices*
1	*tablespoon of coriander pieces*
2	*cups of chicken broth (or water)*

Directions:

1. Scale the fish, cut and discard its head, and remove its internal organs. Rinse and drain.
2. Cut fish into 2-inch segments.
3. Heat vegetable oil in wok over medium heat; then slide in fish segments and fry until both sides turn golden brown.
4. Transfer to a large bowl.
5. Add salt, green onion, and ginger. Then pour in 2 cups of chicken broth (or water).
6. Put the bowl in a large soup pot with water over high heat and steam for a half hour.
7. Remove the bowl, sprinkle sesame oil and coriander pieces over the fish, and serve.

Note: The high cholesterol content of this dish makes it bad for those suffering from cardiovascular diseases.

Crisp Kelp

Medicinal Uses:

Replenishes the blood.
Removes congestion and other stasis in the body
Clears vessels.
Removes excess heat from the body.
Promotes the circulation of body fluids.
Used to treat cardiovascular diseases and diabetes.

Ingredients:

7	*ounces of soaked kelp*
12	*cups of vegetable oil*
2	*tablespoons of starch*
2	*tablespoons of raw sugar*
2	*teaspoons of vinegar*
2	*tablespoons of cooking wine*
1	*cup of wheat flour*
1	*tablespoon of soy sauce*
1/2	*teaspoon of salt*
1/2	*tablespoon of garlic chips*
1	*cup of water*

Directions:

1. Wash the soaked kelp and cut into triangular pieces.
2. Combine wheat flour with 1 cup of water.
3. Coat each kelp piece with flour by dipping it.
4. Heat vegetable oil in wok over high heat; then slide in kelp pieces and deep-fry until brown. Transfer and let stand.
5. Make sauce by mixing soy sauce, vinegar, salt, sugar, cooking wine, and garlic chips.
6. Remove oil from wok leaving only 2 tablespoons.
7. Pour in the sauce and cook until boiling.
8. Slide in fried kelp. Stir to mix several times.
9. Transfer and serve.

Stir-Fried Salmon

Medicinal Uses:
Nourishes the kidney and brain.
Improves vision.
Replenishes the protein needed by the human body.
Aids in the absorption of calcium.
Used to treat obesity, hypertension and diabetes.

Ingredients:

1   *pound of salmon fillet*
2   *cups of vegetable oil*
3   *tablespoons of cooking wine*
2   *tablespoons of soy sauce*
1   *tablespoon of sugar*
1/2 *tablespoon of green-onion chunks (each an inch long)*
1/2 *tablespoon of ginger strips*
2   *cups of water*

Directions:

1. Cut salmon fillet into 5-inch x 2-inch strips.
2. Cover strips in soy sauce and let stand for 10 minutes.
3. Heat vegetable oil in wok over high heat; then slide in salmon strips and deep-fry till they turn brown.
4. Remove and let stand for 10 minutes.
5. Remove vegetable oil from wok, leaving only 2 tablespoons in the wok.
6. Slide in green-onion chunks and ginger strips and stir-fry for 1 minute.
7. Add in 2 cups of water, sugar, cooking wine, and salt. Mix well.
8. Slide in fried salmon strips, reduce the heat, and simmer for 15 minutes.
9. Transfer and serve.

Inkfish With Chives

Medicinal Uses:

Reinvigorates excessive yang energy of the liver and kidney. Cleanses the stomach and intestines.

Treats fatigue due to kidney deficiency and indigestion.

Used to relieve hepatitis, hypertension, and diabetes.

Ingredients:

1/2	*pound of inkfish*
1	*pound of chives*
2	*cloves of garlic*
1/2	*tablespoon of soy sauce*
1/2	*teaspoon of salt*
3	*tablespoons of vegetable oil*

Directions:

1. Cut the inkfish into 2-inch strips.
2. Wash and cut chives into 1-inch strips.
3. Cut garlic into pieces.
4. Heat vegetable oil in wok over high heat; then slide in garlic pieces and stir-fry for 10 minutes.
5. Slide in inkfish strips and stir-fry for 1 minute.
6. Add in chive strips and stir-fry for 5 minutes.
7. Add in salt and soy sauce and mix well for 30 seconds.
8. Transfer and serve.

Mustard Squid Strips

Medicinal Uses:
Stimulates the appetite.
Replenishes energy.
Promotes the circulation of body fluid to relieve swelling. Used to treat hypertension and diabetes.

Ingredients:

1/2 *pound of squid*
1 *tablespoon of mustard*
1 *teaspoon of garlic chips*
1 *tablespoon of vinegar*
1/2 *tablespoon of sugar*
1/2 *teaspoon of salt*
1 *tablespoon of sesame oil*

Directions:

1. Cut squid into 1.5–inch strips and boil in water for 5 minutes.
2. Transfer to a plate and let stand.
3. Make sauce by mixing garlic chips, mustard, vinegar, sugar, salt, and sesame oil.
4. Pour the sauce over squid strips. Mix well and let stand for a half-hour.
5. Serve.

Note: For best results, use fresh squid and do not overcook.

Eel With Pickled Cucumber

Medicinal Uses: ❋

Reverses fatigue.

Removes dampness and gas in the body.

Promotes blood circulation and reduces blood-sugar levels. Used to treat rheumatic arthritis, diabetes, and poor appetite due to spleen and stomach deficiencies.

Ingredients:

 1 *pound of fresh eel*
10 *pieces of pickled cucumber*
1/2 *teaspoon of salt*
 2 *cups of vegetable oil*

Directions:

1. Clean the eel to remove and discard all internal organs.
2. Apply salt inside and outside. Let it stand for 10 minutes.
3. Heat vegetable oil in wok over high heat; then slide in eel and deep-fry for 8 minutes, until eel turns brown.
4. Transfer the eel to a plate and place pickled cucumber pieces around it.
5. Serve.

Perch With Mushroom

Medicinal Uses:

Nourishes the kidney and brain.
Improves vision.
Provides needed protein.
Aids in the absorption of calcium.
Used to treat obesity, hypertension, and diabetes.

Ingredients:

1 *pound of perch*
8 *ounces of mushrooms*
1/4 *teaspoon of salt*
2 *tablespoons of soy sauce*
1 *stalk of green onion*
1/2 *tablespoon of pepper*
2 *tablespoons of sesame oil*
2 *eggs*
4 *tablespoons of vegetable oil*
2 *tablespoons of cooking wine*

Directions:

1. Clean perch and slice into thin slices. Cut mushrooms into slices. Cut green onion into 1-inch chunks.
2. Heat 2 tablespoons of vegetable oil in wok, add green-onion chunks and ginger slices, stir-fry for 15 seconds, and then add salt, soy sauce, pepper, sesame oil, cooking wine, and starch. Mix well to make sauce.
3. Separate eggs and discard yolks. Beat egg whites. Put the perch slices into the egg white.
4. Heat remaining vegetable oil in the wok, add mushroom and perch slices, and stir-fry for 3 minutes.
5. Pour the sauce made in step 2 into the wok. Go on stir-frying for 1 minute.
6. Transfer and serve.

Sautéed Trout

Medicinal Uses:

Nourishes the kidney and brain.
Improves vision.
Restores depleted protein.
Aids in the absorption of calcium.
Used to treat obesity, hypertension, and diabetes.

Ingredients:

1	*pound of trout*
2	*tablespoons of soy sauce*
1/4	*teaspoon of salt*
1	*stalk of green onion*
1/2	*tablespoon of ginger slices*
1	*tablespoon of vinegar*
2	*tablespoons of cooking wine*
1	*tablespoon of sugar*
4	*tablespoons of vegetable oil*
1/2	*cup of water*

Directions:

1. Clean the trout, smear salt inside and outside, and let stand for 10 minutes.
2. Cut green onion into half-inch chunks.
3. Make sauce by mixing sugar, soy sauce, vinegar, cooking wine, and a half-cup of water.
4. Heat 3 tablespoons of vegetable oil in wok over high heat; then slide in trout and fry until both sides turn golden brown. Remove from wok.
5. Add the remaining oil to wok, then slide in green-onion chunks and ginger slices and stir-fry for 10 seconds.
6. Pour in the sauce.
7. Slide the trout into wok, reduce heat to medium, and simmer for 8 minutes.
8. Transfer and serve.

Curry Fish

Medicinal Uses:
Nourishes the kidney and brain.
Improves vision.
Nourishes the stomach and spleen.
Stimulates the appetite.
Replaces depleted protein.
Helps in the absorption of calcium.
Used to treat obesity, hypertension, and diabetes.

Ingredients:

1   *pound of any fish fillet*
1 1/2   *cups of cooking wine*
2   *tablespoons of curry powder*
1   *ounce of onion*
1   *teaspoon of salt*
3   *tablespoons of vegetable oil*

Directions:

1. Cut onion into slices.
2. Marinade fillet into cooking wine for 5 minutes.
3. Heat 2 tablespoons of vegetable oil in wok over high heat; then slide in fish fillet and fry until brown.
4. Remove fish and let stand.
5. Add remaining vegetable oil to wok; then slide in onion slices and stir-fry for 2 minutes.
6. Add curry powder, 1 cup of water, and salt to wok.
7. After it boils, remove and pour the sauce over the fish fillets on the plate.
8. Serve.

Fish Fillet With Asparagus

Medicinal Uses:

Nourishes the kidney and brain.
Improves vision.
Replenishes protein.
Aids in the absorption of calcium.
Clears away excessive body heat.
Promotes the production of body fluid to remove swelling.
Used to treat obesity, hypertension, and diabetes.

Ingredients:

4	ounces of any fish fillet
2	ounces of asparagus
2	cups of vegetable oil
2	tablespoons of cooking wine
2	tablespoons of starch
2	eggs
1	stalk of green onion
1/2	tablespoon of ginger chips
1/2	tablespoon of garlic chips
1/2	teaspoon of salt

Directions:

1. Cut fish fillet into 1-inch x 1-inch slices.
2. Cut asparagus into 1-inch x 1-inch slices.
3. Cut green onion into 1-inch chunks.
4. Dissolve starch in a half-cup of water.
5. Separate yolk from eggs and beat egg white only.
6. Combine fish fillet with egg whites.
7. Heat vegetable oil in wok over high heat; then slide in fish fillet and deep fry until each piece floats.
8. Remove fish from wok, drain off excess oil, and let stand.
9. Remove oil from wok, leaving only 2 tablespoons in wok.
10. Add in ginger, garlic, and green onion and stir-fry quickly for 15 seconds.
11. Slide in asparagus pieces and stir-fry for 2 minutes.
12. Add in salt, cooking wine, and 1 cup of water.

13. When mixture in wok boils, pour in dissolved starch. Stir several times to thicken sauce.
14. Slide in fish fillets again and mix well with sauce in wok.
15. Transfer and serve.

Sautéed Codfish

Medicinal Uses:
Nourishes the kidney and brain.
Improves vision.
Replenishes protein.
Helps the body absorb needed calcium.
Use to treat obesity, hypertension, and diabetes.

Ingredients:

1	*pound of codfish*
2	*cups of vegetable oil*
3	*tablespoons of cooking wine*
2	*tablespoons of soy sauce*
1	*tablespoon of sugar*
1/2	*tablespoon of green-onion chunks*
1/2	*tablespoon of ginger strips*
1/3	*teaspoon of salt*
2	*cups of water*

Directions:

1. Clean codfish to remove internal organs.
2. Coat fish in soy sauce inside and out. Let it stand for 10 minutes.
3. Heat vegetable oil in wok over high heat; then slide in fish and deep-fry until it turns brown. Remove fish.
4. Remove vegetable oil from wok, leaving only 2 tablespoons in the wok.
5. Slide in green-onion chunks and ginger strips to stir-fry for 1 minute. Put in 2 cups of water, sugar, cooking wine, and salt. Mix well.
6. When the sauce in wok is boiling, slide in fried fish again. Reduce to low heat and simmer for 10 minutes.
7. Transfer and serve.

Crucian With Green Onion

Medicinal Uses:

Promotes the passage of body fluids.

Nourishes the stomach, liver, and brain.

Promotes milk production in women after delivery.

Reduces swelling.

Used to treat hepatitis, hypertension, and diabetes.

Ingredients:

1–1.5 *pounds of Crucian Fish*

1 *ounce of green onion*

1/2 *ounce of fresh coriander*

1/2 *teaspoon of salt (divided in half)*

2 *tablespoons of soy sauce*

2 *tablespoons of vegetable oil*

Directions:

1. Clean the fish and remove its head and tail.
2. Cut green onion into 2-inch chunks.
3. Cut coriander into 1-inch strips.
4. Boil fish in water for 10 minutes; then add half the salt.
5. Remove fish and sprinkle remaining salt on both sides; then put it on a plate.
6. Add green onion and coriander and pour soy sauce on the fish.
7. Heat vegetable oil in wok over high heat; then sprinkle the hot oil over the fish body.
8. Transfer and serve.

Fish Fillet With Cucumber

Medicinal Uses:

Nourishes the kidney and brain.

Improves vision.

Provides needed protein.

Helps the absorption of calcium.

Clears away excessive heat in the body.

Promotes the circulation of body fluid.

Removes toxins from the body.

Used to treat obesity, hypertension, cancer, and diabetes.

Ingredients:

5 *ounces of fish fillet*

2 *ounces of cucumber*

2 *cups of vegetable oil*

2 *tablespoons of cooking wine*

2 *tablespoons of starch*

2 *eggs*

1 *stalk of green onion*

1/2 *tablespoon of ginger chips*

1/2 *tablespoon of garlic chips*

1/2 *teaspoon of salt*

1 *cup of water*

Directions:

1. Cut fish fillet into 1-inch x 1-inch slices.
2. Cut cucumber into 1-inch x 1-inch slices.
3. Cut green onion into 1-inch chunks.
4. Dissolve starch in 1/2 cup of water.
5. Separate egg whites from yolk. Discard yolk and beat egg whites.
6. Combine fish fillet with egg whites.
7. Heat vegetable oil in wok over high heat; then slide in fish fillet and deep fry until each piece floats on oil surface. Remove fish and drain oil.
8. Remove oil from wok, leaving only 2 tablespoons in wok.
9. Add in ginger, garlic, and green onion and stir-fry quickly for 15 seconds.
10. Slide in cucumber pieces and stir-fry for 2 minutes.

11. Add in salt, cooking wine, and 1 cup of water.
12. When mixture boils, pour in dissolved starch. Stir several times to make sauce thicker.
13. Slide fish fillets into wok again and mix well with sauce.
14. Transfer and serve.

Sautéed Conch Slices

Medicinal Uses:
Nourishes the kidney and brain.
Improves vision.
Provides needed protein.
Helps with the absorption of calcium.
Used to treat obesity, hypertension, and diabetes.

Ingredients:

7 *ounces of conch meat*

1 *ounce of pepper oil*

3 *tablespoons of sesame oil*

2 *tablespoons of soy sauce*

1/4 *teaspoon of salt*

1/2 *teaspoon of pepper*

1 *tablespoon of green-onion chips*

Directions:

1. Slice the conch meat and boil in water for 10 minutes.
2. Remove fish, drain, and allow to cool.
3. Make sauce by mixing pepper oil, sesame oil, soy sauce, salt, pepper, and chopped green onion.
4. Pour the sauce over the conch slices.
5. Mix well and serve.

Sweet and Sour Crisp-skin Crucian Fish

Medicinal Uses:

Promotes milk production in women after birth.

Used to treat hepatitis, swelling, hypertension, and diabetes.

Ingredients:

1–1.5 *pounds of crucian fish*

1.5 *ounces of raw sugar*

1.2 *ounces of vinegar*

4 *tablespoons of cooking wine*

3 *tablespoons of soy sauce*

2 *tablespoons of starch*

2 *stalks of green onion*

1 *tablespoon of ginger strips*

1/2 *teaspoon of garlic chips*

1 *teaspoon of salt (divided in half)*

4 *tablespoons of maize flour*

1 *cup of vegetable oil*

Directions:

1. Clean the fish and make 3 cuts on each back.
2. Smear 1/2 teaspoon of salt over the fish and let stand for 10 minutes.
3. Combine maize flour with water and mix well.
4. Dip the fish into the mixture and coat completely.
5. Cut green onion into 1-inch chunks.
6. Make sauce by mixing sugar, vinegar, soy sauce, cooking wine, remaining salt, and starch.
7. Heat vegetable oil in wok over high heat; then slide in fish coated with flour and deep-fry for 8 minutes, until it turns brown.
8. Transfer fish to a plate.
9. Drain oil from wok, leaving only 2–3 tablespoons.
10. Slide in ginger, garlic, and green onion and stir-fry for 10 seconds.
11. Pour in the sauce and cook for 3 minutes.
12. Pour the hot sauce over the fish.
13. Serve.

Gingered Carp

Medicinal Uses:
Promotes the passage of body fluids.
Nourishes the stomach, liver, and brain.
Provides necessary protein.
Reverses poor appetite caused by stomach and spleen deficiencies.
Used to treat hepatitis.
Useful for treating hypertension.

Ingredients:

1–1.5 pounds of carp fish
1.5 ounces of fresh ginger
1 ounce of vinegar
2/3 ounce of sesame oil
2 tablespoons of soy sauce
1 teaspoon of salt (divided in half)
2 tablespoons of cooking wine (divided in half)
1 stalk of green onion
1 teaspoon of ginger slices

Directions:
1. Clean the fish and make 3 cuts on each side.
2. Cut green onion into 1 1/2 -inch chunks.
3. Boil fish in water for 5 minutes. Remove and drain.
4. Smear 1/2 teaspoon of salt and 1 tablespoon of cooking wine on fish. Let fish stand for 10 minutes.
5. Place fish on a plate and put green-onion chunks and ginger slices on its back.
6. Put the plate into a pot with water and steam it over high heat for 10 minutes.
7. Remove the plate and keep the ginger and green onion.
8. Chop the ginger into chips; then mix it with vinegar, sesame oil, the remaining salt, and soy sauce.
9. Pour the sauce over the steamed fish.
10. Serve.

Note: Caution — This dish should be avoided if you have a cough with yellow phlegm.

Jellyfish and Turnip

Medicinal Uses:

Invigorates the stomach to improve digestion.

Smoothes the lungs to clear congestion.

Reduces blood pressure.

Promotes the circulation of body fluid.

Used to treat hypertension, stomach burn, enlargement of the thyroid gland due to iodine shortage, and chronic bronchitis.

Ingredients:

- 3 *ounces of jellyfish*
- 8 *ounces of turnip*
- 1/2 *teaspoon of salt*
- 1 *tablespoon of soy sauce*
- 1 *tablespoon of raw sugar*
- 1 *tablespoon of vinegar*
- 1 *tablespoon of sesame oil*
- 1/2 *tablespoon of green-onion chips*

Directions:

1. Wash and shave turnip.
2. Cut turnip into thin strips, combine salt, mix well, and let stand for one day.
3. Wash jellyfish; then immerse in water for 3 hours.
4. Rewash and drain fish.
5. Place fish in hot water and soak for 10 minutes.
6. Cut jellyfish into thick strips.
7. Rinse fish again with cold water. Drain and let stand.
8. Drain off saltwater from turnip.
9. Mix turnip with jellyfish strips.
10. Mix soy sauce, raw sugar, vinegar, sesame oil, and green-onion chips.
11. Add sauce with turnip and fish and mix well.
12. Serve.

Turnip With Shrimp

Medicinal Uses:
Helps the circulation of body fluid.
Nourishes the kidney.
Treats loin and knee pain due to kidney deficiency.
Strengthens the bones and muscles.
Used to treat osteoporosis.

Ingredients:

1	*pound of turnip*
1/2	*ounce of dried small shrimp*
2	*tablespoons of vegetable oil*
1	*tablespoon of starch*
2	*tablespoons of soy sauce*
1/2	*teaspoon of salt*
1/2	*tablespoon of raw sugar*
1/2	*tablespoon of green-onion chips*
1	*cup of warm water*

Directions:
1. Clean turnip and cut into 1/2-inch cubes.
2. Wash dried shrimp and drain.
3. Boil turnip cubes in water for 5 minutes.
4. Remove turnip and cool down.
5. Heat vegetable oil in wok over high heat; then slide in dried shrimps and green-onion chips, followed by turnip cubes. Stir-fry for 3 minutes.
6. Add in sugar, salt, and a cup of warm water. Reduce to low heat and simmer for 7 minutes.
7. Dissolve starch in water and pour over the turnip cubes in the wok. Mix well.
8. Transfer and serve.

Shrimp With Tomato Sauce

Medicinal Uses:
Nourishes the stomach and spleen.
Stimulates poor appetite due to stomach deficiency, such as ulcers.

Ingredients:

1/2	*pound of cleaned shrimp*
2	*tablespoons of tomato sauce*
1	*egg*
2	*tablespoons of vegetable oil (divided in half)*
1	*teaspoon of raw sugar*
1/2	*teaspoon of salt (divided in half)*
15	*pieces of snow peas*
2	*teaspoons of starch (divided in half)*
1	*tablespoon of cooking wine*
1/2	*tablespoon of sesame oil*
1	*cup of water*

Directions:
1. Put shrimp in a bowl. Beat in egg and add half the salt and 1 teaspoon starch. Mix well.
2. Heat 1 tablespoon of vegetable oil in the wok over high heat; then slide in shrimp and fry until golden.
3. Transfer to a plate and let stand.
4. Put remaining oil in wok and heat over medium heat; then slide in tomato sauce and snow peas and stir-fry for 2 minutes.
5. Add in cooking wine, sugar, remaining salt, and 1 cup of water.
6. When it boils, add in remaining starch.
7. Slide in shrimp and stir several times.
8. Remove, sprinkle sesame oil on it, and serve.

Sweet and Sour Yellow Croaker

Medicinal Uses:

Improves the appetite.

Nourishes the liver.

Helps with hepatitis, especially during the recovery period.

Used to treat hypertension, diabetes, and high cholesterol.

Ingredients:

1	*yellow croaker*
1/2	*pound of tofu*
1	*stalk of garlic sprout**
1	*tablespoon of fresh coriander*
1/2	*tablespoon of pepper*
1	*tablespoon of cooking wine*
4	*tablespoons of vegetable oil (divided in half)*
1	*tablespoon of sugar*
4	*tablespoons of vinegar*
1/2	*tablespoon of ginger strips*
1/2	*tablespoon of green-onion pieces*
1/2	*teaspoon of salt*
4	*teaspoons of soy sauce (divided in half)*
2	*cups of water*

Directions:

1. Scale the yellow croaker and remove gills. Remove internal organs through gills. Cut out dorsal fin.
2. Wash croaker and put it in a bowl. Pour 2 teaspoons of soy sauce over it and let stand.
3. Cut garlic into 1-inch strips.
4. Cut coriander into thick pieces.
5. Cut tofu into half-inch cubes.
6. Heat 2 tablespoons of vegetable oil in wok over high heat; then slide in croaker and fry until golden.
7. Transfer to a plate and let stand.
8. Heat remaining vegetable oil in wok over high heat; then slide in ginger and green onion and stir-fry quickly for 10 seconds.

9. Slide croaker back into wok; then combine cooking wine, raw sugar, remaining soy sauce, and 2 cups of water.
10. When it boils, reduce heat and simmer for 10 minutes.
11. Turn heat up to high; then add in tofu, salt and a cup of water. Cook until it boils.
12. Combine vinegar, pepper, coriander, and garlic sprout in a soup basin.
13. Pour sauce, croaker, tofu, and soup into bowl.
14. Serve.

Note: * When planted, garlic cloves sprout chive-like shoots that can be used as seasoning. You can purchase them in an Oriental grocery store.

Vegetarian Dishes

Eggs With Chives

Medicinal Uses:
Treats male impotence and premature ejaculation.
Fights loin and knee pain and frequency of urination caused by a kidney deficiency.
Improves digestion.

Ingredients:

5.3 *ounces of fresh chives*
2 *eggs*
1 *tablespoon of vegetable oil (divided in half)*
1/2 *teaspoon of salt (divided in half)*

Directions:

1. Wash chives and cut into 1-inch strips.
2. Break eggs into a bowl and mix evenly with chopsticks; then add half the salt.
3. Heat 1/2 tablespoon vegetable oil in the wok over medium heat; then pour in whipped egg.
4. When egg turns solid, remove from wok, break into large pieces, and place in a bowl.
5. Heat remaining oil in wok over high heat; then add chive strips and stir-fry for 5 minutes.
6. Add egg pieces to wok.
7. Fry for another 2 minutes; then add the remaining salt.
8. Transfer and serve.

Chinese Cabbage in Vinegar

Medicinal Uses:
Used for constipation.
Treats cough.
Treats bleeding of the stomach and intestines.
Useful in treating obesity.

Ingredients:

- 1 *cup of Chinese cabbage*
- 1 *tablespoon of soy sauce*
- 1 *tablespoon of vinegar*
- 1/4 *teaspoon of salt*
- 1/2 *tablespoon of green-onion chips*
- 1/4 *tablespoon of ginger chips*
- 1 *tablespoon of vegetable oil*
- 1 *tablespoon of cornstarch*
- 2/3 *cup of water*

Directions:

1. Wash and cut cabbage into 1-inch pieces.
2. Chop ginger and green onion into pieces.
3. Put ginger and green onion in a bowl and add in soy sauce, salt, vinegar, cornstarch, and 2/3 cup of water. Mix well and let stand.
4. Heat vegetable oil in wok over high heat; then slide in cabbage pieces and stir-fry for 5 minutes.
5. Pour in mixed sauce and stir-fry for another minute, until cabbage and sauce are well mixed.
6. Transfer and serve.

Sweet and Sour Cabbage Rolls

Medicinal Uses:

Nourishes the spleen and stomach.
Improves the appetite.
Used to treat those with high cholesterol and/or those suffering from cardiovascular diseases.

Ingredients:

1	*cup of cabbage*
1/4	*cup of carrots*
1/4	*cup of bamboo shoots*
4	*pieces of dried red chili*
1	*stalk of green onion*
1	*piece of ginger*
1/2	*teaspoon of salt*
4	*teaspoons of vinegar*
4	*teaspoons of sugar*
2	*tablespoons of vegetable oil*
1	*cup of water*

Directions:

1. Cut carrots and bamboo shoots into matching strips.
2. Cut green onions and ginger into thick strips.
3. Soak dried red chili in warm water until soft; then remove the seeds and cut into thick strips.
4. Put cabbage leaves in hot water to boil until done.
5. Transfer to cool water to cool down. Drain.
6. Boil carrot and bamboo-shoot strips for 1 minute. Drain, transfer, and let stand.
7. Heat vegetable oil in wok over high heat; then slide in red-pepper, ginger, and green-onion strips and stir-fry for 15 seconds.
8. Pour in 1 cup of water; then add vinegar, sugar, and salt.
9. Cook until it boils; then transfer the soup to a large bowl to cool down.
10. Soak cooked cabbage leaves in the cooled soup for 30 minutes.
11. Put carrot and bamboo-shoot strips in the middle of the cabbage leaves and wrap each leaf into a roll.
12. Cross-cut the rolls into 2-inch pieces. Arrange the cut rolls on a plate and serve.

Chinese Cabbage With Mushrooms

Medicinal Uses:

Smoothes the stomach and intestines.
Promotes the circulation of body fluid.
Used to treat constipation and intestinal bleeding.
Useful for treating hypertension, heart disease, and diabetes.

Ingredients:

1   *pound of Chinese cabbage*
1/2   *pound of mushrooms*
2   *tablespoons of vegetable oil (divided in half)*
1/2   *teaspoon of salt*
1   *tablespoon of soy sauce*
2   *teaspoons of sesame oil*
2   *tablespoons of cooking wine*
1   *tablespoon of green-onion chips (divided in half)*
1/2   *tablespoon of garlic chips*
1/2   *tablespoon of ginger strips*

Directions:

1. Wash cabbage and cut into 1-inch x 1-inch pieces.
2. Wash mushrooms and cut each into 4 sections.
3. Heat 1 tablespoon of vegetable oil in wok over high heat; then slide in 1/2 tablespoon of green onion and stir-fry for 10 seconds.
4. Add in cabbage pieces and stir-fry for 3 minutes. Transfer to a plate and let stand.
5. Heat another tablespoon of vegetable oil over high heat; then slide in mushroom pieces and stir-fry for 3 minutes.
6. Add in soy sauce and cooking wine. After mixing well, slide in cabbage pieces and stir-fry for 3 minutes.
7. Drop in remaining green onion, garlic, and ginger. Sprinkle sesame oil. Mix well.
8. Transfer and serve.

Chinese Cabbage With Sesame Paste

Medicinal Uses:
  Replenishes calcium.

Ingredients:
  1 *pound of heart of Chinese cabbage*
  2 *ounces of sesame paste*
  2 *tablespoons of vinegar*
  2 *teaspoons of sugar*
  2 *tablespoons of sesame oil*

Directions:
  1. Clean the cabbage, heat, and cut into 2-inch strips; place them on a plate.
  2. Combine sesame paste with sesame oil, mix well and pour over the cabbage strips.
  3. Sprinkle sugar and vinegar over the cabbage strips. Stir to mix evenly.

Gingered Spinach

Medicinal Uses:

Promotes blood circulation.

Stimulates the production of stomach fluid.

Nourishes the intestines to improve digestion.

Used to treat constipation and excessive thirst due to internal dryness, anemia, hypertension, and hemorrhoids.

Ingredients:

8 *ounces of spinach*

1 *tablespoon of ginger juice**

2 *tablespoons of vinegar*

1 *stalk of green onion*

1/2 *teaspoon of salt*

1/2 *tablespoon of cornstarch*

2 *tablespoons of vegetable oil*

1/2 *tablespoon of sesame oil*

Directions:

1. Wash spinach and cut it in half down the middle.
2. Cut the green onion into 1-inch chunks.
3. Make sauce by mixing ginger juice, vinegar, salt, cornstarch, and a cup of water. Then sprinkle sesame oil over the mixed sauce.
4. Heat vegetable oil in wok over high heat. Slide in green-onion chunks and stir-fry for 15 seconds.
5. Slide in spinach and cook for 5 minutes.
6. Pour the sauce over the spinach and continue stir-frying quickly for 1 minute.
7. Transfer to a plate to serve.

Note: * You can purchase bottled ginger juice or make your own. To make ginger juice peel a large slice of fresh ginger, grate it on a hand grater, pack it into a garlic press, and squeeze out the juice.

Wok-fried Tomatoes

Medicinal Uses:
Stimulates poor appetite.
Reverses thirst due to excessive interior body heat.

Ingredients:

10	ounces of tomatoes
3	eggs
1	teaspoon of salt
1/2	tablespoon of green-onion chips
1/2	tablespoon of ginger chips
3	ounces of chicken broth
5	ounces of cornstarch
3	ounces of vegetable oil

Directions:

1. Wash tomatoes and cross-cut into quarter-inch-thick slices.
2. Beat and whip eggs.
3. Dissolve a half-ounce of cornstarch in water.
4. Spread remaining dry cornstarch on a flat plate and coat tomato slices with it.
5. Heat 2.5 ounces of vegetable oil in a wok over high heat.
6. Dip tomato slices in egg; then slide into the wok to fry till brown. Transfer to a plate.
7. Heat remaining oil over high heat; then add the ginger and green-onion pieces, followed by chicken broth and salt. Then add the dissolved cornstarch to thicken the broth.
8. Pour thick broth over fried tomato slices.
9. Transfer and serve.

Mushrooms With Garlic

Medicinal Uses:

Nourishes yin energy.
Moistens dryness in the body.
Reinvigorates the stomach and spleen.
Used to treat aleukia, chronic hepatitis, hypertension, heart disease, diabetes, and cancer.

Ingredients:

1	pound of mushrooms
1	ounce of garlic
3	teaspoons of soy sauce
2	tablespoons of cooking wine
1/2	tablespoon of pepper
1/4	teaspoon of salt
2	tablespoons of cornstarch
2	tablespoons of vegetable oil

Directions:

1. Clean mushrooms and cut into slices.
2. Cut garlic into thin slices.
3. Put a wok with a half-gallon of water over high heat.
4. When water boils, put in mushroom slices and cook for 3 minutes. Then drain and transfer mushrooms to a plate.
5. Heat vegetable oil over high heat. Add in garlic slices, soy sauce, and 3 cups of water.
6. Add in mushroom slices and salt.
7. When it boils, reduce to low heat and simmer for 7 minutes.
8. Add in cornstarch and stir quickly to make the soup in the wok thicker.
9. Transfer and serve.

Egg and Tomato Sauté

Medicinal Uses:

Improves the appetite.

Quenches thirst due to excess heat.

Increases gastric acid.

Used to treat heatstroke, hypertension, and chronic hepatitis.

Ingredients:

3   *eggs*

3   *tomatoes*

1.8   *ounces of cooking oil*

1/2   *teaspoon of salt (divided in half)*

1/2   *tablespoon of cooking wine*

1/2   *tablespoon of sugar*

Directions:

1. Scald tomatoes in boiling water to remove peel.
2. Cut tomatoes into thick slices. Put them in a bowl and let stand.
3. Break eggs into a bowl and whip. Add in half the salt and 1/2 tablespoon of cooking wine and mix evenly.
4. Heat cooking oil over high heat. Slide in tomato slices and stir-fry for 2 minutes. Then add the remaining salt and 1/2 tablespoon of sugar.
5. Pour in egg mixture and continue stir-frying for another 2 minutes.
6. Transfer and serve.

Note: Caution – Those who suffer from high cholesterol and arthritis should avoid this dish.

Turnip Sauté

Medicinal Uses:

Relieves extravagated blood.
Smoothes vital energy to improve digestion.
Promotes fluid passage to remove toxic material.
Prevents cancer.

Ingredients:

10.6 *ounces of turnip*
2 *teaspoons of raw sugar*
2 *teaspoons of vinegar*
1/3 *teaspoon of salt*
1/2 *teaspoon of soy sauce*
1/4 *tablespoon of ginger slices*
1/4 *tablespoon of green-onion chips*
1/2 *tablespoon of sesame oil*

Directions:

1. Peel the turnip and cut into thin slices.
2. Combine salt with turnip slices and let sit for 6 hours.
3. Drain out salt water.
4. Add sugar, vinegar, ginger slices, green-onion chips and sesame oil to turnip slices. Mix well.
5. Let sit for another 30 minutes before serving.

Egg With Spinach

Medicinal Uses:
Promotes blood circulation.
Cleanses the stomach and intestines.
Adjusts vital energy.
Stops restlessness.
Quenches thirst.
Lubricates the lungs.
Used to treat constipation and a sense of thirst due to internal dryness, anemia, hypertension, and hemorrhoids.

Ingredients:

2   *egg whites*
1   *ounce of dried shrimp*
1   *pound of spinach*
2   *teaspoons of soy sauce*
2   *tablespoons of vegetable oil*
2   *teaspoons of starch*
1   *teaspoon of mustard*
1   *tablespoon of sesame paste*
1   *tablespoon of vinegar*
1/2 *tablespoon of garlic chips*
1/4 *teaspoon of salt*
1   *cup of water*

Directions:

1. Beat egg whites in a bowl and whip; then combine starch and salt. Mix well.
2. Soak dried shrimp in warm water for 5 minutes. Remove and drain.
3. Wash spinach and boil it in water for 3 minutes.
4. Remove to let cool down; then cut into 1-inch strips. Put spinach strips on a plate.
5. Heat 2 tablespoons of vegetable oil in a pan. Add egg and tilt the pan so the egg completely covers the bottom. Cook over medium heat until the egg is set. Loosen edges and flip the egg to cook the other side.
6. Remove the egg pancake, cut it into match strips, and put them over the spinach strips.

7. Put soaked dry shrimps over the spinach and egg strips.
8. Combine mustard and sesame paste with 1 cup of water. Mix well. Then add in soy sauce, garlic, and vinegar.
9. Pour the sauce over the spinach.
10. Serve.

Fresh Corn With Hot Green Pepper

Medicinal Uses:

Promotes the production of body fluid to remove swelling. Nourishes the stomach to relieve constipation.
Used to treat indigestion, hypertension, and diabetes.

Ingredients:

5   *ounces of fresh corn*
1   *ounce of hot green pepper*
1/2   *teaspoon of salt*
3   *tablespoons of vegetable oil*

Directions:

1. Wash fresh corn.
2. Wash hot green peppers and cut them diagonally into 2-inch strips.
3. Heat a wok over medium heat (no oil in this step); then put in pepper strips and dry-fry for 2 minutes, until the strips shrink. Remove and let stand.
4. Heat vegetable oil in wok over high heat. Slide in corn and stir-fry for 3 minutes.
5. Add in pepper strips and go on stir-frying for 2 minutes; then add salt and mix well.
6. Transfer and serve.

Egg With Cucumber

Medicinal Uses:

Provides essential protein and vitamins.
Clears away heat.
Promotes the circulation of body fluid.
Proves useful for those on a diet.

Ingredients:

   2 *eggs*
1/2 *pound of cucumber*
   1 *tablespoon of green-onion chips*
   2 *tablespoons of vegetable oil (divided in half)*
1/2 *teaspoon of salt*
   1 *tablespoon of starch*

Directions:

1. Wash and cut cucumber into 1/8-inch pieces.
2. Dissolve starch in 1/2 cup of water.
3. Beat and whip eggs in a bowl.
4. Heat 1 tablespoon of vegetable oil in wok over medium heat. Add in egg and stir-fry till it sets.
5. Slice egg into 1-inch pieces. Remove and let stand.
6. Heat remaining oil over high heat; then slide in cucumber pieces and stir-fry for 2 minutes.
7. Add in egg pieces, green-onion chips, and melted starch.
8. Add in salt and stir-fry for 1 minute.
9. Transfer and serve.

Crisp and Hot Cucumber Strips

Medicinal Uses:

Clears away excessive body heat.

Promotes the circulation of body fluid

Removes toxins.

Helps reduce throat swelling and pain, thirst, and vomiting due to pathogenic heat.

Useful for treating obesity and diabetes.

Ingredients:

2   *cucumbers*

1   *tablespoon of soy sauce*

1   *tablespoon of vegetable oil*

1/2   *teaspoon of salt*

1/2   *teaspoon of sugar*

1   *piece of hot red chili*

Directions:

1. Wash cucumbers and cut in half. Remove seeds; then cut into 2-inch chunks.
2. Combine with salt to stand for 1 hour. Drain off salt water.
3. Heat vegetable oil in wok over medium heat; then slide in red chili to fry for 10 seconds, until it browns.
4. Add in cucumber chunks, soy sauce, and sugar.
5. Increase to high heat and stir-fry quickly for 1 minute.
6. Transfer and serve.

Fried Hot Green Pepper

Medicinal Uses:

Stimulates the appetite.
Helps to reduce blood pressure.
Used to treat cardiovascular diseases.

Ingredients:

5 *hot green peppers*

3 *tablespoons of vegetable oil*

2 *tablespoons of soy sauce*

1 *tablespoon of sugar*

1 *tablespoon of vinegar*

1/4 *teaspoon of salt*

1/2 *tablespoon green-onion chips*

Directions:

1. Wash and drain hot green peppers.
2. Make sauce by combining soy sauce, vinegar, sugar, salt, and green onion. Mix well and let stand.
3. Heat vegetable oil in wok over medium heat; then slide in peppers and fry until brown (there should be bubbles on the surface.)
4. Pour the sauce over peppers.
5. Reduce to low heat, cover the wok, and let simmer for 1 minute.
6. Transfer and serve.

Note: Caution – Those with stomach or intestinal problems should avoid this dish.

Golden Fried Wheat Flour Tea

Medicinal Uses:

Nourishes spleen to stimulate the appetite.
Nourishes the skin.
Promotes hair growth.
Removes congestion, constipation, and wakefulness.
Relieves cough.
Useful in treating heart disease, hypertension, and cancer.

Ingredients:

  1   *pound of wheat flour*
  5   *teaspoons of olive oil*
10   *ounces of almonds*
  1   *teaspoon of salt*

Directions:

1. Grind almonds into powder.
2. Combine wheat flour with olive oil.
3. Put the mixture in a pan over low heat and stir-fry until brown.
4. Add in almond powder and salt. Mix well.
5. To serve mix 2 teaspoons of the wheat flour mixture and with a glass of water and heat. Serve as you would tea.

Sesame Celery

Medicinal Uses:

Protects and clears blood vessels.
Reduces blood pressure.
Protects blood capillaries.
Used to treat hypertension, arteriosclerosis, and obesity.

Ingredients:

1	*pound of celery*
1	*tablespoon of sesame oil*
1/4	*teaspoon of salt*
2	*teaspoons of soy sauce*

Directions:

1. Clean celery and cut into 1-inch strips.
2. Boil celery strips in water for 2 minutes.
3. Remove from water; combine with sesame oil, salt, and soy sauce.
4. Mix well and serve.

Note: Caution – Those with ulcers should avoid this dish.

Avocado with Tomato

Medicinal Uses:
Lubricates the intestines.
Used to treat obesity, constipation and those with weak stomachs and intestines.

Ingredients:

1/3 pound of avocado
1/3 pound of tomato
  2 cloves of garlic
1/2 tablespoon of basil
  2 tablespoons of olive oil
  2 tablespoons of soy sauce

Directions:

1. Peel avocado and cut into 1/3-inch cubes.
2. Wash tomato and cut into 1/3-inch cubes.
3. Cut tofu into 1/3-inch cubes.
4. Crush garlic and chop into small chips.
5. Put avocado, tofu, and tomato cubes in a bowl. Sprinkle on soy sauce, basil, and olive oil.
6. Mix well and serve.

Bitter Melon With Soybeans

Medicinal Uses:

Helps to reduce blood pressure.
Calms the gallbladder.
Used to treat asthma, insomnia, and cancer.

Ingredients:

- 1 *pound of bitter melon*
- 3 *ounces of soybeans*
- 2 *teaspoons of soy sauce*
- 1 *tablespoon of sesame oil*
- 1/4 *teaspoon of salt*
- 1/2 *tablespoon of vinegar*

Directions:

1. Cut each bitter melon in half; then remove seeds and chop into slices.
2. Boil bitter-melon strips in water for 2 minutes.
3. Remove and let stand on a plate.
4. Boil soybeans in water for 15 minutes, until done.
5. Remove soybeans and place on bitter-melon strips.
6. Sprinkle soy sauce, sesame oil, salt, and vinegar.
7. Mix well and serve.

Sesame Spinach

Medicinal Uses:
Used to treat hypertension and diabetes.
Good for treating obesity.

Ingredients:

1	pound of spinach
1	ounce of sesame seeds
2	teaspoons of soy sauce
1/4	teaspoon of salt
1	clove of garlic
1	teaspoon of vinegar

Directions:
1. Wash spinach and cut into 2-inch strips.
2. Crush garlic and then chop into thin chips.
3. Boil spinach strips in water for 2 minutes. Remove and drain.
4. Sprinkle on sesame seeds, soy sauce, vinegar, and garlic chips.
5. Mix well and serve.

Bitter Melon With Hot Red Chili

Medicinal Uses:

Calms the liver.

Nourishes the gallbladder.

Improves vision.

Used to treat hypertension, diabetes, and high cholesterol.

Ingredients:

1/2　*pound of bitter melon*

3　*pieces of hot red chili*

1　*tablespoon of olive oil*

1/2　*teaspoon of salt*

1　*section of garlic*

Directions:

1. Cut each bitter melon in half and remove the seeds; then chop into slices.
2. Crush garlic and chop into thin chips.
3. Heat olive oil over high heat; slide in red chili and garlic chips and stir-fry for 5 seconds, until you can smell their fragrance.
4. Slide in bitter-melon strips and stir-fry for 3 minutes.
5. Add in salt, stir, and mix well.
6. Transfer and serve.

Sweet and Sour Cucumbers

Medicinal Uses:

Harmonizes the blood vessels.

Disperses blood stasis.

Improves digestion.

Clears away heat and toxins in the body.

Helps to reduce cholesterol.

Useful in treating hypertension, heart disease, and obesity.

Ingredients:

2   *fresh cucumbers*

2   *tablespoons of vinegar*

1   *tablespoon of raw sugar*

1/4   *teaspoon of salt*

1   *tablespoon of soy sauce*

1/2   *tablespoon of mashed garlic*

1   *tablespoon of sesame oil*

Directions:

1. Wash cucumber; then cut off and discard two ends.
2. Cut cucumber into thin slices and put them on a plate.
3. Add salt to cucumbers and mix well. Let stand for 2 hours.
4. Drain off water infused from cucumber slices.
5. Add vinegar, sugar, mashed garlic, soy sauce, and sesame oil.
6. Mix well and serve.

Cucumber With Garlic

Medicinal Uses:

Harmonizes the blood vessels.
Disperses blood stasis.
Improves digestion.
Clears away heat and toxins from the body.
Helps to reduce cholesterol and high blood pressure.
Useful for treating diabetes and obesity.

Ingredients:

1   *pound of cucumber*
1.5 *ounces of garlic*
1/2 *teaspoon of salt*
2   *tablespoons of sesame oil*
2   *tablespoons of vinegar*

Directions:

1. Wash cucumbers; then slice in half along their middles.
2. Smash each half with a knife and then cut into cubes. Set cubes on a plate and let stand.
3. Chop garlic into thin pieces. Combine with salt, sesame, vinegar and mix well.
4. Pour the sauce over the cucumbers.
5. Mix well and serve.

Cucumber With Coriander and Hot Green Pepper

Medicinal Uses:

Promotes the natural movements of the stomach and intestine.
Stimulates poor appetite caused by interior heat due to stomach and spleen deficiencies.
Used to treat hypertension, diabetes, and those who are sick from ingesting to many oily
foods.

Ingredients:

1.2   *ounces of fresh coriander*

  3   *ounces of cucumber*

  6   *ounces of hot green pepper*

1/2   *teaspoon of salt*

  2   *tablespoons of sesame oil*

Directions:

1. Cut coriander into chips.
2. Cut cucumber and pepper into fingernail-size pieces.
3. Mix coriander chips, cucumber, and pepper. Sprinkle on salt and sesame oil.
4. Mix well and serve.

Turnips and Crushed Garlic

Medicinal Uses:

Invigorates the stomach to improve digestion.

Clears away congestion.

Kills viruses and helps to reduce blood pressure.

Resolves blood stasis.

Used to treat chest congestion and excess phlegm.

Useful in treating obesity.

Ingredients:

1 *bulb of garlic (with purple peel)*

8 *ounces of turnip*

1/4 *teaspoon of salt*

1 *tablespoon of soy sauce*

1/2 *tablespoon of vinegar*

1 *tablespoon of sesame oil*

Directions:

1. Wash and shave turnip; then cut it into thin strips.
2. Combine turnip with 1/4 teaspoon of salt, mix well and let stand for one day.
3. Crush garlic with a knife and remove the peel.
4. Drain off saltwater from turnip.
5. Combine smashed garlic, soy sauce, vinegar, and sesame oil.
6. Mix well and serve.

Sweet Potato and Corn Congee

Medicinal Uses:

Warms the interior.

Nourishes the stomach and spleen.

Improves digestion.

Ideal for post-illness recovery.

Ingredients:

1/2   *pound of sweet potato*

3   *ounces of dried corn*

Directions:

1. Grind dried corn into coarse chips.
2. Shave sweet potatoes and cut into large cubes.
3. Put a pot with 1/2 gallon of water over high heat.
4. When water boils, reduce to low heat and add in corn chips to cook for 1 hour.
5. Add in sweet-potato cubes and go on cooking for another half-hour, until it seems as if the cubes are melting.
6. Transfer and serve.

Note: Caution – Since sweet potatoes and corn contain relatively high amounts of starch, anyone with diabetes should avoid this dish.

Tofu in Tomato Sauce

Medicinal Uses:

Invigorates the spleen.

Stimulates the appetite.

Improves the production of body fluid to quench thirst. Helps to improve digestion.

Clears away heat.

Promotes the circulation of body fluid.

Used to treat hypertension, obesity, high cholesterol, and poor appetite due to stomach deficiency.

Ingredients:

10 *ounces of tofu*

1 *ounce of tomato sauce*

1/2 *teaspoon of salt*

1 *tablespoon of vinegar*

1/2 *tablespoon of sugar*

1/2 *tablespoon of green-onion chips*

1/2 *tablespoon of ginger chips*

2 *tablespoons of vegetable oil*

5 *ounces of water*

Directions:

1. Cut tofu into half-inch cubes; then boil in water for 1 minute.
2. Heat vegetable oil in wok over high heat. Slide in ginger and green-onion chips and stir-fry for 15 seconds.
3. Add in tomato sauce and stir-fry for 30 seconds.
4. Pour in 5 ounces of water.
5. Add in salt, vinegar, sugar, and tofu cubes.
6. Cook until it boils.
7. Transfer and serve.

Tofu With Green Onion

Medicinal Uses:
Clears away interior heat.
Nourishes the stomach.
Used to treat poor appetite due to hot weather.

Ingredients:
1/2   *pound of tofu*
4   *stalks of green onion*
1/2   *teaspoon of salt*
1   *tablespoon of sesame oil*

Directions:
1. Cut tofu into half-inch cubes.
2. Wash green onion and cut into thin pieces.
3. Mix tofu, sesame oil, salt, and green-onion pieces together.
4. Serve.

Spiced-up Celery

Medicinal Uses:

Protects and clears blood vessels.

Reduces blood pressure and protects blood capillaries.

Used to treat hypertension, arteriosclerosis, obesity, and diabetes.

Ingredients:

1	*pound of fresh celery*
1/4	*teaspoon of salt*
1	*tablespoon of soy sauce*
1	*tablespoon of vinegar*
1	*tablespoon of sesame oil*

Directions:

1. Remove celery root and leaves. Wash and drain.
2. Put a wok with 1/2 gallon of water over high heat until boiling.
3. Add in celery and cook for 6 minutes.
4. Transfer celery to a plate and let it cool down.
5. Cut celery into 1-inch strips; then place in a large bowl.
6. Add salt, vinegar, soy sauce, and sesame to celery.
7. Mix well and serve.

Note: Not for those with hypopiesis and ulcers

Spinach and Celery in Sesame Oil

Medicinal Uses:

Nourishes Ying.

Clears away heat.

Calms the liver.

Reduces pressure and bloating.

Improves urination.

Lubricates intestines and loose bowls.

Used to treat hypertension characterized by symptoms like headaches, dizziness, flushing, constipation, and restlessness.

Useful in treating diabetes.

Ingredients:

- 8 *ounces of spinach*
- 8 *ounces of celery*
- 2 *tablespoons of sesame oil*
- 1/2 *teaspoon of salt*

Directions:

1. Remove celery leaves and roots. Wash spinach and celery.
2. Boil celery and spinach (separately) in water for 2 minutes each.
3. Remove celery and spinach and cut into 1-inch chunks.
4. Transfer vegetables to a plate.
5. Combine salt and sesame oil with celery and spinach.
6. Mix well and serve.

Hot Green Pepper With Bitter Melon

Medicinal Uses:

Provides vitamin C.

Clears away heat.

Removes toxins.

Lowers blood sugar.

Used to treat diabetes, hypertension, and high cholesterol.

Ingredients:

3	ounces of hot green pepper
8	ounces of bitter melon
1	tablespoon of vinegar
1	tablespoon of soy sauce
1/4	teaspoon of salt
1	stalk of green onion
2	tablespoons of vegetable oil

Directions:

1. Cut green pepper into thin strips.
2. Cut the bitter melon in half and remove seeds; then slice into pieces.
3. Cut green onion into half-inch chunks.
4. Put pepper strips and bitter-melon pieces into a wok and dry-fry (no oil) for 3 minutes.
5. Pour vegetable oil into the wok; then slide in green onion, soy sauce, and salt.
6. Stir-fry for 5 minutes.
7. Sprinkle on vinegar and remove to serve.

Bitter Melon in Red-pepper Oil

Medicinal Uses:

Clears away interior heat.

Removes toxins

Lowers blood sugar.

Used to treat diabetes, hypertension, obesity, and high cholesterol.

Ingredients:

1/2 *pound of bitter melon*

2/3 *ounce of red-pepper oil*

1/4 *teaspoon of salt*

1 *tablespoon of soy sauce*

2 *tablespoons of sesame oil*

1/2 *tablespoon of green-onion chips*

Directions:

1. Cut each bitter melon into two halves and remove seeds.
2. Cut diagonally into thin strips.
3. Put a wok with 1/4 gallon of water over high heat. When it's boiling, put in bitter melon to boil 4 minutes. Remove to drain and let cool down.
4. Make sauce by mixing salt, soy sauce, sesame oil, and green-onion chips.
5. Pour the sauce over the bitter-melon strips.
6. Mix well to serve.

String Beans in Ginger Juice

Medicinal Uses:

Warms the interior.
Lubricates the lungs to resolve congestion.
Treats cough.
Removes toxins.
Stimulates movement of the stomach to improve digestion.
Strengthens the stomach.
Suppresses vomiting.
Helps to improve appetite.
Clears away heat from the body.
Used to treat hypertension and diabetes.

Ingredients:

1   *pound of string beans*
1   *ounce of ginger*
1   *ounce of vinegar*
1   *teaspoon of salt*
3   *tablespoons of sesame oil*

Directions:

1. Clean string beans.
2. Put 1 gallon of water in a wok over high heat until boiling.
3. Add in string beans and boil 10 minutes.
4. Transfer string beans to a bowl of cold water to cool. Once cooled down, drain water from bowl.
5. Add salt to beans and let stand for 5 minutes. Drain off any excess water.
6. Chop ginger into thin pieces.
7. Make sauce by mixing ginger pieces, vinegar, and sesame oil.
8. Sprinkle the sauce over string beans.
9. Mix well and let the beans stand for 10 minutes.
10. Serve.

Lotus Root With Green Onion

Medicinal Uses:
Invigorates the stomach and spleen.
Nourishes blood.
Used to treat chronic hepatitis, and gastroduodenal ulcer.

Ingredients:
1   *pound of lotus root*
2   *stalks of green onion*
1/2 *teaspoon of salt*

Directions:
1. Shave lotus root and cut into thin slices.
2. Put 1 gallon of water in a wok over high heat till boiling.
3. Add in lotus-root slices and boil for 10 minutes.
4. Transfer lotus-root slices to a bowl of cold water to cool. Drain and put on a plate.
5. Chop green onion into thin pieces.
6. Make sauce by mixing green-onion pieces and sesame oil.
7. Sprinkle the sauce over the lotus-root slices.
8. Mix well and serve.

Lotus Root in Ginger Juice

Medicinal Uses:
Warms the body.
Lubricates the lungs to resolve congestion.
Treats coughs.
Removes toxins.
Stimulates the movement of the stomach to improve digestion.
Strengthens the stomach and spleen.
Suppresses vomiting.
Used to treat stomach deficiency with symptoms like ache, indigestion, and bleeding.

Ingredients:

1.2	*ounces of ginger*
8	*ounces of lotus root*
3	*tablespoons of sesame oil*
1	*tablespoon of soy sauce*
1/4	*teaspoon of salt*
2	*teaspoons of vinegar*

Directions:
1. Shave lotus root and cut into thin slices.
2. Put 1 gallon of water in a wok over high heat till boiling.
3. Add in lotus-root slices and boil for 10 minutes.
4. Shave the ginger; then slice and chop it into chips.
5. Make sauce by mixing ginger chips, soy sauce, salt, sesame oil, and vinegar.
6. Pour the sauce over the lotus-root slices.
7. Mix well to serve.

Green Bell Pepper With Green Bean Sprouts

Medicinal Uses:

Clears away heat.
Promotes circulation of body fluid.
Used to treat hypertension and diabetes, especially in summer.

Ingredients:

1/2 pound of green bean sprouts

7 ounces of green bell pepper

1 teaspoon of salt

2 tablespoons of vegetable oil

Directions:

1. Wash bean sprouts and pepper.
2. Cut pepper into thick strips.
3. Heat vegetable oil in wok over high heat. Slide in pepper strips and stir-fry for 3 minutes.
4. Slide in green bean sprouts.
5. Add in salt and continue stir-frying for another 2 minutes.
6. Remove and serve.

Green Bean Sprouts With Chives

Medicinal Uses:
Reinvigorates the kidney.
Purges pathogenic heat and toxins.
Used to treat hypertension, diabetes and fatigue in the loins and knees due to kidney deficiency.
Useful in treating obesity.

Ingredients:

1/2	*pound of green bean sprouts*
3	*ounces of chives*
1/2	*teaspoon of salt*
1	*tablespoon of vegetable oil*

Directions:

1. Wash green bean sprouts and drain.
2. Wash chives and cut into 1-inch strips.
3. Heat vegetable oil in wok over high heat. Slide in green bean sprouts and chives together.
4. Stir-fry for 4 minutes.
5. Add in salt and mix well.
6. Remove and serve.

Sweet and Sour Yellow Bean Sprouts

Medicinal Uses:

Rich in plant protein.
Used to treat hypertension, cardiovascular diseases, edema, and constipation.

Ingredients:

1 *pound of yellow bean sprouts*
3 *teaspoons of raw sugar*
2 *teaspoons of vinegar*
1 *teaspoon of salt*
2 *tablespoons of sesame oil*
1 *tablespoon of green-onion pieces*

Directions:

1. Wash bean sprouts and drain.
2. Boil bean sprouts in water for 1 minute. Remove and drain.
3. Make sauce by combining salt, vinegar, sesame oil, and sugar.
4. Sprinkle sauce over the bean sprouts.
5. Mix well and serve.

Celery, Kelp, and Carrot

Medicinal Uses:

Clears burning and heat away from the kidneys.
Promotes blood circulation.
Calms the liver.
Clears congestion.
Reduces blood pressure.
Lowers cholesterol.
Acts as a cancer preventive.
Useful for treating obesity.

Ingredients:

7 *ounces of celery*

1.8 *ounce of kelp*

3.5 *ounces of carrot*

2 *tablespoons of vegetable oil*

1 *teaspoon of soy sauce*

2 *tablespoons of cooking wine (divided in half)*

1/2 *teaspoon of salt*

1 *stalk of fennel*

Directions:

1. Soak kelp in cold water for 1 hour.
2. Wash kelp and soak it again in warm water for a half-hour.
3. Cut kelp in large pieces and transfer to a small soup pot.
4. Add enough cold water to immerse the kelp.
5. Simmer over medium heat for a half-hour.
6. Add 1 tablespoon of cooking wine, 1 teaspoon of soy sauce, and fennel. Reduce to low heat and simmer another half-hour.
7. Remove to cool down; then cut kelp into strips and let stand.
8. Remove roots and leaves from celery; then wash and shake off attached water.
9. Cut into half-inch stems and let stand.
10. Wash carrot and cut into thin strips.
11. Heat wok over high heat; then slide in carrots and dry-fry (no oil) for 8 minutes. Remove and let stand.
12. Heat vegetable oil over medium heat and cook celery for 5 minutes.
13. Slide in carrot strips; then add remaining cooking wine and 1/2 teaspoon of salt and stir-fry for another 3 minutes.

14. Slide in kelp strips and add 2 tablespoons of water.
15. Simmer for 5 minutes.
16. Sprinkle on scallion pieces.
17. Remove and serve.

Steamed Eggplant

Medicinal Uses:
Dissolves extravagated blood.
Eliminates edema.
Stops bleeding
Induces diuresis.
Enhances the functions of blood capillaries.
Useful for treating hypertension.

Ingredients:
4 *eggplants*
1/4 *teaspoon of salt*
1 *tablespoon of soy sauce*
1 *tablespoon of sesame oil*
1 *tablespoon of green-onion chips*

Directions:
1. Wash the eggplants; then cut each into four large pieces and put them into a large bowl.
2. Put the bowl into a soup pot with water. Fill with just enough water to cover the bottom of the bowl but not cause it to float.
3. Steam for 20 minutes and then remove the bowl.
4. While the eggplant is hot, sprinkle on salt, soy sauce, sesame oil and or scallion pieces.
5. Mix evenly and serve.

String Beans, Tomato, and Tofu

Medicinal Uses:
Used to treat hypertension, diabetes, and chronic fatigue.

Ingredients:

1.8	ounces of fresh tofu
2	tomatoes
0.7	ounces of string beans
1	tablespoon of vegetable oil
1/2	tablespoon of starch
0.07	ounces of dried shrimp
1/2	teaspoon of salt
4	tablespoons of water

Directions:

1. Boil string beans in water for 1 minute. Drain and let stand.
2. Cut tofu into 1-inch x 1-inch strips.
3. Boil tofu in water for 1 minute. Drain and let stand.
4. Cut tomato into small sections.
5. Soak dried shrimp for half an hour. Drain and let stand.
6. Heat vegetable oil in the wok over high heat; then stir-fry scallions and ginger for 10 seconds.
7. Slide in tomato pieces and stir-fry for 1 minute.
8. Add 4 tablespoons of water, slide in tofu, dried shrimp, and string beans. Stir-fry for 5 minutes.
9. Add salt, remove, and serve.

Yellow Bean Sprout Sauté

Medicinal Uses:

Nourishes the spleen and stomach.
Clears blood vessels.
Removes swellings.
Nourishes the large intestines.
Reduces cholesterol.
Used to treat cardiovascular disease, hypertension, edema, and constipation.

Ingredients:

1.1 *pounds of bean sprouts*

2 *tablespoons of vegetable oil*

1/2 *teaspoon of salt*

1/2 *tablespoon of soy sauce*

1 *tablespoon of cooking wine*

1/2 *tablespoon of green-onion pieces*

1/2 *bowl of water*

Directions:

1. Remove roots from sprouts. Wash and drain.
2. Heat vegetable oil over high heat; then slide in bean sprouts, and stir-fry for 5 minutes.
3. Add salt, cooking wine, and soy sauce; then stir-fry for another 3 minutes.
4. Add a half bowl of water, cover the wok, and simmer for 6 minutes.
5. Sprinkle in green-onion pieces and continue stir-frying for another 2 minutes.
6. Remove and serve.

Peanuts and Celery

Medicinal Uses:
Restores blood vessels.
Lowers blood pressure.
Reduces gas and bloating.
Improves vision.
Calms the mind.
Induces diuresis.

Ingredients:

0.7 ounces of peanuts

0.9 ounces of celery

1/2 teaspoon of salt

1/2 tablespoon of soy sauce

1/4 tablespoon of sugar

1/2 tablespoon of vinegar

1 tablespoon of cooking oil

1/4 tablespoon of pepper oil

Directions:

1. Heat cooking oil in a pan for 1 minute.
2. Add peanuts, fry until crispy, and move to a plate.
3. Cut celery into 1-inch strips.
4. Boil celery in water for 30 seconds; then remove and rinse in cold water. Drain off any excess water.
5. Arrange the celery around the plate and place peanuts at the center.
6. Put soy sauce, salt, sugar, vinegar, and pepper oil into a small bowl and mix well.
7. Pour the mixture onto the dish and serve.

Three Cubes Sautéed

Medicinal Uses:
Clears away heat.
Restores blood circulation.
Helps improve the appetite.
Useful for treating hypertension.

Ingredients:

3.5 *ounces of dried white bean curd*
3.5 *ounces of snow peas*
1 *red pepper*
1 *tablespoon of vegetable oil*
1/2 *tablespoon of soy sauce*
1/4 *tablespoon of sugar*
1/4 *teaspoon of salt*
0.2 *ounce of ginger*
0.3 *ounce of onion*
1/2 *tablespoon of starch*
2 *tablespoons of water*

Directions:

1. Cut red peppers and dried white bean curd into half-inch cubes.
2. Put dried bean curd into boiling water. Put snow peas into a separate pot of boiling water. Allow both to boil for a brief time then drain the water.
3. Put cooking oil into the pan and heat for about 1 minute. Add onion and ginger into pan.
4. Add bean curd and fry for 1 minute.
5. Add red pepper, snow peas, soy sauce, sugar, salt and 2 tablespoons of water.
6. Dissolve starch with a little bit of water and add to the mixture.
7. Turn off the stove.
8. Remove and serve.

Stir-fried Mushrooms With Celery

Medicinal Uses:
Clears away heat.
Calms the liver.
Replenishes qi and blood.
Used to treat hypertension and diabetes.

Ingredients:

1	*pound of celery*
1.8	*ounces of water soaked mushrooms*
1	*tablespoon of vegetable oil*
1/2	*teaspoon of salt*
1/2	*tablespoon of vinegar*
1/2	*tablespoon of soy sauce*
1/2	*tablespoon of starch*
2	*ounces of water*

Directions:

1. Cut celery into 1-inch strips.
2. Mix celery with salt and let stand for about 10 minutes. Rinse and drain.
3. Cut mushrooms into pieces.
4. Put starch, vinegar, and 2 ounces of water into a bowl to make a thin paste.
5. Stir-fry the celery in hot oil for 2 or 3 minutes; then put in mushroom pieces and stir-fry quickly.
6. Add soy sauce and stir for 1 minute.
7. Add in paste and mix well.
8. Remove and serve.

Hot and Sour Potato Strips

Medicinal Uses:
Stimulates poor appetite caused by stomach or intestinal disorders.

Ingredients:

  1/2 *pound of potatoes*
   2   *tablespoons of vinegar*
   4   *pieces of red chili*
  1/2 *teaspoon of salt*
   2   *tablespoons of vegetable oil*

Directions:
1. Peel potatoes and cut into thin strips.
2. Rinse with cold water to remove starch on the surface, drain, and transfer potato strips to a plate.
3. Cut red chili into thin strips.
4. Heat vegetable oil in wok over high heat; then slide in chili and stir-fry for 5 seconds.
5. Slide in potato strips and stir-fry for 8 minutes.
6. Sprinkle vinegar over the strips and mix well.
7. Remove and serve.

Hot Green Pepper With Potato Strips

Medicinal Uses:

Stimulates the appetite.
Reinvigorates the stomach.
Used to treat loin pain due to weak stomach, fatigue, and constipation.
Useful in treating hypertension and heart disease.

Ingredients:

1/2 *pound of hot green peppers*
1/2 *pound of potatoes*
 1 *teaspoon of salt*
1/2 *tablespoon of pepper*
 3 *tablespoons of vegetable oil*

Directions:

1. Wash hot green peppers and potatoes.
2. Cut them into match-size strips.
3. Rinse potato strips to remove starch on the surface. Drain and let stand.
4. Heat vegetable oil in wok over high heat; then slide in peppers and stir-fry until you can smell their fragrance. Remove peppers and discard.
5. Add in potato strips and pepper and stir-fry for 8 minutes.
6. Add salt and mix well.
7. Remove and serve.

Celery and Potato Strips

Medicinal Uses:
Strengthens the stomach.
Used to treat stomachache, chronic constipation, vomiting,
gastroduodenal ulcers, hypertension, and diabetes.

Ingredients:

1	*pound of potatoes*
1.8	*ounces of celery*
0.8	*ounce of fresh red pepper*
2	*tablespoons of vegetable oil*
1	*tablespoon of soy sauce*
1/2	*tablespoon of sesame oil*
1/2	*tablespoon of vinegar*
1/4	*teaspoon of salt*
1	*stalk of green onion*
1/2	*tablespoon of sugar*

Directions:

1. Peel the potatoes and cut into match strips. Do the same with the red pepper and green onions.
2. Remove celery leaves and root. Cut into 1-inch strips.
3. Drop the potatoes into boiling water for half a minute. Cool down with cold water. Drain and let them stand.
4. Make sauce by mixing salt, sugar, vinegar, and soy sauce.
5. Heat vegetable oil in wok over high heat. Fry green-onion strips quickly and then add in potatoes, celery, and red pepper. Stir-fry for 10 minutes.
6. Sprinkle in mixed sauce. Fry for 1 more minute.
7. Remove and serve.

Bamboo Shoots With Green Onions

Medicinal Uses:

Promotes circulation of blood and other body fluids.
Quenches thirst due to excess interior heat.
Used to treat hypertension and diabetes.

Ingredients:

7 *ounces of bamboo shoots*

3 *stalks of green onion*

1/2 *teaspoon of salt*

2 *tablespoons of sesame oil*

4 *tablespoons of hot water*

Directions:

1. Wash bamboo shoots and cut into match-size strips.
2. Boil in water for 3 minutes; then remove, drain, and let stand on a plate.
3. Wash green onions and cut into thin chips.
4. Make sauce by mixing salt, sesame oil, and 4 tablespoons of hot water.
5. Sprinkle the sauce over bamboo shoots.
6. Mix well and serve.

Hot Green Peppers With Bamboo Shoots

Medicinal Uses:

Promotes circulation of blood and other body fluids.
Quenches thirst due to excess interior heat.
Used to treat hypertension and diabetes.

Ingredients:

> 5 *ounces of hot green peppers*
> 10 *ounces of bamboo shoots*
> 1/2 *teaspoon of salt*
> 2 *tablespoons of sesame oil*
> 1 *tablespoon of vegetable oil*

Directions:

1. Wash peppers and cut into rings.
2. Cut bamboo shoots into match-size strips.
3. Boil pepper rings and bamboo-shoot strips in water for 3 minutes; then drain and let stand on a plate.
4. Heat vegetable oil and sesame oil in wok over high heat.
5. Pour the heated oil over the pepper pieces and bamboo-shoot strips on the plate.
6. Combine salt and mix well.
7. Remove and serve.

Spicy Radishes

Medicinal Uses:
Purges heat.
Nourishes blood.
Promotes the circulation of body fluid.
Used to treat hypertension, constipation, and swelling.
Acts as a cancer preventive.

Ingredients:

1 *pound of red radishes*

3 *teaspoons of soy sauce*

3 *teaspoons of red chili oil*

2 *tablespoons of sesame oil*

1/4 *teaspoon of salt*

1 *teaspoon of sugar*

Directions:

1. Wash radishes and cut into thin strips.
2. Add salt to radishes and allow to stand for 10 minutes. Drain off the salt-water.
3. Make sauce by mixing red-chili oil, soy sauce, sesame oil, and sugar.
4. Sprinkle the sauce over the radish strips.
5. Mix well and serve.

Chinese Broccoli Sauté

Medicinal Uses:
Clears away heat.
Promotes the circulation of body fluid.
Nourishes stomach and intestines.
Used to treat indigestion, obesity, and thirst due to overheating of the
stomach and spleen.

Ingredients:
- 1 *pound of Chinese broccoli*
- 2 *teaspoons of garlic chips*
- 2 *tablespoons of vegetable oil*
- 1/2 *teaspoon of salt*

Directions:
1. Wash Chinese broccoli and drain.
2. Heat vegetable oil over high heat; then slide in garlic chips, and stir-fry for 10 seconds.
3. Slide in Chinese broccoli and stir-fry for 5 minutes.
4. Add in salt and mix well.
5. Remove and serve.

Asparagus Lettuce Strips in Sesame Paste

Medicinal Uses:
 Promotes the production of body fluid.
 Purges interior heat.
 Used to treat hypertension, diabetes, indigestion, and osteoporosis.

Ingredients:
  1 *pound of asparagus lettuce*
  2 *tablespoons of sesame oil*
  2 *tablespoons of sesame paste*
  1/2 *teaspoon of salt*
  1/2 *tablespoon of sugar*
  1/2 *cup of warm water*

Directions:
  1. Cut lettuce into thin strips.
  2. Boil lettuce strips in water for 1 minute; then drain and let stand on a plate.
  3. Combine sesame paste with 1/2 cup of warm water; then add salt, sugar and sesame oil.
  4. Pour the sauce over the lettuce strips.
  5. Mix well and serve.

Note: This lettuce, which looks like a cross between celery and lettuce, can be found in any Chinese grocery store and some mainstream groceries.

Succulent Asparagus-lettuce Strips

Medicinal Uses:
Nourishes the stomach and spleen.
Stimulates the appetite.
Promotes the production of body fluid.
Clears away heat.
Used to treat hypertension and diabetes.
It is a good dish for and those who are on diet.

Ingredients:

- 1 *pound of asparagus lettuce*
- 3 *teaspoons of coriander chips*
- 1 *teaspoon of green-onion chips*
- 1/2 *tablespoon of pepper*
- 1 *teaspoon of raw sugar*
- 1 *tablespoon of sesame paste*
- 3 *teaspoons of soy sauce*
- 1 *teaspoon of vinegar*
- 2 *teaspoons of red-chili oil*
- 1/2 *teaspoon of salt*
- 2 *tablespoons of sesame oil*
- 1/2 *tablespoon of Garlic chips*

Directions:

1. Shave the lettuce and cut into thin strips.
2. Combine the strips with salt and a cup of warm water and soak for 5 minutes.
3. Make sauce by mixing sesame paste, soy sauce, vinegar, sesame oil, pepper, sugar, garlic chips, and coriander.
4. Pour the sauce over the lettuce strips.
5. Mix well and serve.

Carrot Sautéed in Butter

Medicinal Uses:
Invigorates the lungs.
Acts as a stomach and spleen tonic.
Dries dampness and removes congestion.
Provides heat to defend against cold.
Used to treat stomach and spleen deficiencies.

Ingredients:

10 *ounces of carrots*

2 *tablespoons of cooking wine*

1/4 *teaspoon of salt*

1/2 *tablespoon of pepper*

1/2 *ounce of onion*

2 *tablespoons of butter*

1/2 *cup of water*

Directions:

1. Shave the carrot and cut into thin strips.
2. Boil strips in water for 5 to 6 minutes (being careful not to make them too tender), drain, and let stand.
3. Cut green onion into strips.
4. Heat butter in wok over medium heat; slide in onion strips and stir-fry for 5 minutes, until they turn brown.
5. Slide in carrot strips and add salt, pepper, and a half-cup of water.
6. Cover the wok and simmer over medium heat for 5 minutes.
7. Remove and serve.

Green Hot Pepper With Eggplant

Medicinal Uses:
   Protects blood vessels.
   Promotes circulation of body fluids.
   Used to treat cardiovascular diseases and swelling.

Ingredients:

   3   *ounces of hot green peppers*
   1/2   *pound eggplant*
   4   *tablespoons of vegetable oil*
   1   *tablespoon of soy sauce*
   1/3   *teaspoon of salt*
   1/3   *teaspoon of pepper*
   1   *tablespoon of green-onion chips*
   1   *tablespoon of garlic chips*

Directions:

1. Clean the hot green peppers and remove seeds.
2. Cut peppers into match-size strips.
3. Wash the eggplant and cut into match-size strips.
4. Heat vegetable oil in wok over high heat, slide in green-onion chips, and pepper. Stir-fry for 10 seconds.
5. Slide in eggplant strips to stir-fry for 5 minutes.
6. Slide in green-hot-pepper strips and continue to stir-fry for another 3 minutes.
7. Add soy sauce and salt and stir-fry for 1 minute.
8. Remove and serve.

Eggplant With Potatoes

Medicinal Uses:

Helps with stomach weakness.
Improves the functions of stomach and intestines.
Protects blood vessels.
Used to treat chronic fatigue, constipation, and cardiovascular diseases.

Ingredients:

1   *pound of eggplant*
1   *pound of potatoes*
2   *eggs*
1   *tablespoon of coriander chips*
1/2   *teaspoon of salt (divided in half)*
1   *tablespoon of sesame oil*

Directions:

1. Wash eggplant and potatoes.
2. Place in a bowl and steam over boiling water for 30 minutes.
3. Remove their peels and smash them into paste.
4. Combine eggplant and potato paste with half the salt and mix well.
5. Boil eggs; then remove the shells and separate the yolks from the whites.
6. Smash the yolks into paste and chop the whites into thin pieces.
7. Divide remaining salt and add 1/2 to the yolk paste and sprinkle other 1/2 over egg white pieces.
8. Put eggplant and potato paste in the center of a plate, and yolk paste and white chips beside them on each side.
9. Sprinkle on sesame oil and coriander chips.
10. Serve.

Eggplant Strips Sauté

Medicinal Uses:

Protects blood vessels.

Promotes the circulation of body fluids.

Used to treat cardiovascular disease, hypertension, diabetes, obesity, and swelling.

Ingredients:

10	*ounces of eggplant*
4	*tablespoons of vegetable oil*
2	*tablespoons of soy sauce*
1/4	*teaspoon of salt*
1/2	*teaspoon of pepper*
1/2	*tablespoon of garlic chips*
1/2	*tablespoon of green-onion chips*

Directions:

1. Clean eggplant and cut into match-size strips.
2. Soak eggplant strips in cold water for 3 minutes, and remove to drain.
3. Heat vegetable oil in wok over high heat; then slide in pepper, garlic, and green-onion chips. Stir-fry for 10 seconds.
4. Slide in eggplant strips and stir-fry for 8 minutes.
5. Add in soy sauce and salt; then stir-fry for 1 more minute.
6. Remove and serve.

Mixed Vegetable Omelet

Medicinal Uses:
Replenishes protein.
Replenishes vital energy.
Used to treat chronic fatigue due to kidney and stomach deficiencies.

Ingredients:

  2 *eggs*
  7 *ounces of squash*
  2 *ounces of onion*
  2 *stalks of green onion*
  2 *ounces of hot green pepper*
  2 *tablespoons of olive oil*
1/2 *tablespoon of pepper*

Directions:

1. Wash and cut squash, onion, and green onion into 1/3-inch cubes.
2. Cut hot green pepper into fingernail-size slices.
3. Beat and whip eggs.
4. Mix egg with squash, green onion, and onion cubes.
5. Combine with olive, pepper, and hot-green-pepper pieces. Mix well.
6. Put a pan over medium heat; then pour in egg mixture to completely cover pan bottom.
7. When egg mixture is set, loosen edges and flip egg to cook other side.
8. When both sides are set, remove to serve.

Bitter Melon With Soybeans

Medicinal Uses:
Reduces blood pressure.
Calms the gallbladder.
Used to treat asthma, cancer, and wakefulness.

Ingredients:

1	*pound of bitter melon*
3	*ounces of soybeans*
2	*teaspoons of soy sauce*
1	*tablespoon of sesame oil*
1/2	*teaspoon of vinegar*

Directions:

1. Cut each bitter melon in half, remove seeds, and then chop into slices.
2. Boil bitter-melon strips in water for 2 minutes; then remove and set aside.
3. Put soybeans in boiling water to cook for 15 minutes.
4. Remove soybeans and cover with better-melon strips.
5. Sprinkle on soy sauce, sesame oil, and vinegar.
6. Mix well and serve.

Cauliflower in Stewed Sauce

Medicinal Uses:
Serves as an ideal food for preventing cancer.
Replenishes needed vitamins.
Used to treat cancer, hypertension, and diabetes.

Ingredients:

1.1 *ounces of cauliflower*
1 *small carrot*
5 *dried mushrooms*
2 *tablespoons of vegetable oil*
1 *tablespoon of soy sauce*
1/2 *tablespoon of cooking wine*
1/2 *teaspoon of sugar*
1/4 *teaspoon of salt*
1/2 *tablespoon of pepper oil*
1/2 *tablespoon of cornstarch*
1/2 *tablespoon of green-onion chips*
2 *tablespoons of water*

Directions:

1. Break off cauliflower into small chunks.
2. Cut carrot into slices.
3. Soak dried mushrooms for 1 hour.
4. Boil carrot and soaked mushrooms in hot water for 1 minute. Remove, drain and let stand.
5. Heat vegetable oil in wok over high heat; then slide in chopped green onion followed by cauliflower, carrot, and mushrooms. Stir-fry for 3 minutes.
6. Add in cooking wine, salt, sugar, soy sauce and 2 tablespoons of water. Stew until fluid in wok boils.
7. Dissolve cornstarch in water then add. Sprinkle on pepper oil.
8. Remove and serve.

Simple Sesame Tofu

Medicinal Uses:

Lubricates intestines.

Provides rich plant protein.

Serves as an ideal food for those suffering from hypertension, diabetes, and for those whoare on a diet.

Ingredients:

1 *pound of tofu*

2 *tablespoons of soy sauce*

1 *tablespoon of sesame oil*

Directions:

1. Cut tofu into 1-inch cubes.
2. Mix soy sauce and sesame oil.
3. Dip tofu cubes into the mixture of soy sauce and sesame oil before eating.

Tofu Strips With Garlic

Medicinal Uses:

Promotes the production of body fluid.

Provides protein needed by the human body.

Helps to clean the stomach and intestines.

Is an ideal food for those suffering from hypertension or diabetes, and for those who are on a diet.

Ingredients:

1/2	*pound of tofu strips*
3	*cloves of garlic*
2	*tablespoons of soy sauce*
1	*tablespoon of vinegar*

Directions:

1. Crush garlic and chop it into thin chips.
2. Mix garlic chips, soy sauce, and vinegar.
3. Sprinkle the mixture over tofu strips.
4. Mix well and serve.

Shredded Green Bell Pepper and Eggplant

Medicinal Uses:

Relieves blood stasis, swelling, and pain.

Is high in Vitamin P, which can enhance cells' adhesion and improve the resistance of small blood vessels to viruses.

Used to treat blood-vessel diseases like hypertension, hemoptysis, and arteriosclerosis.

Ingredients:

1   *green bell pepper*
1   *eggplant*
2   *tablespoons of vegetable oil*
1   *teaspoon of soy sauce*
1/3   *teaspoon of salt*
1/2   *tablespoon of cornstarch*
1/2   *tablespoon of green-onion chips*
1/2   *tablespoon of garlic chips*

Directions:

1. Wash and cut green bell pepper and eggplant into match-size strips.
2. Heat oil in wok over high heat; then slide in green onion, followed by eggplant strips, and stir-fry for 3 minutes.
3. Slide in pepper strips and continue frying for another 5 minutes.
4. Add soy sauce and salt, followed by cornstarch dissolved in water.
5. Add in garlic chips and mix well.
6. Remove and serve.

Spinach Sauté

Medicinal Uses:
Promotes blood circulation.
Cleans the stomach and intestines.
Adjusts vital energy.
Stops restlessness.
Quenches thirst.
Lubricates the lungs.

Ingredients:

1	*pound of spinach*
2	*tablespoons of vegetable oil*
1	*tablespoon of soy sauce*
1/4	*teaspoon of salt*
1/2	*tablespoon of sugar*

Directions:

1. Wash the spinach (keeping red roots) and drain.
2. Heat oil in wok over high heat and add in spinach.
3. Stir-fry for 1 minute.
4. Add soy sauce, sugar, and salt. Mix well.
5. Remove and serve.

Spinach With Sesame

Medicinal Uses:

Serves as an ideal food for hypertension, diabetes, and those who are on a diet.

Ingredients:

1 *pound of spinach*

1 *ounce of sesame oil*

2 *tablespoons of soy sauce*

1/4 *teaspoon of salt*

1 *section of garlic*

1 *teaspoon of vinegar*

Directions:

1. Wash spinach and cut into 2-inch strips.
2. Crush garlic and chop in thin pieces.
3. Put spinach strips into boiling water; then cook for two minutes, remove and drain.
4. Sprinkle sesame oil, soy sauce, vinegar, and garlic chips over the spinach.
5. Mix well and serve.

Sweet and Sour Kelp

Medicinal Uses:

Nourishes the blood and qi.

Clears congestion and other obstructions.

Softens blood vessels.

Clears away excessive heat from the body.

Helps to lower blood cholesterol.

Prevents fat accumulation.

Used to treat arteriosclerosis, hypertension, swollen glands, and edema.

Ingredients:

1/2   *pound of soaked kelp*

1/2   *tablespoon of soy sauce*

1   *tablespoon of vinegar*

1/2   *tablespoon of sugar*

1/4   *teaspoon of salt*

1/2   *tablespoon of sesame oil*

1   *tablespoon of hot sauce (optional)*

Directions:

1. Cut kelp into 3-inch-long strips and put into a large bowl.
2. Add soy sauce, vinegar, sugar, and salt. Mix well.
3. Add hot sauce to taste.
4. Add sesame oil, mix well, and serve.

Sautéed String Beans

Medicinal Uses:
Balances nutrition.
Used to treat hypertension, chronic fatigue, and diabetes.

Ingredients:
- 1.2 *ounces of string beans*
- 1 *ounce of vegetable oil*
- 1/4 *teaspoon of salt*
- 1 *teaspoon of soy sauce*
- 1/2 *tablespoon of green-onion chips*
- 1/2 *tablespoon of garlic chips*
- 5 *tablespoons of water*

Directions:
1. Wash and break string beans into 1-inch strips.
2. Heat vegetable oil in wok over high heat; then slide in green-onion chips and stir-fry for 10 seconds.
3. Slide in string beans and stir-fry for 5 minutes.
4. Add in soy sauce, salt, and 5 tablespoons of water. Cover the wok, reduce to low heat, and simmer for 10 minutes.
5. Add in garlic chips and turn up to high heat. Continue stir-frying for 2 minutes.
6. Remove and serve.

Fried Eggplant

Medicinal Uses:
Protects blood vessels.
Used to treat blood vessel diseases like hypertension, hemoptysis, and arteriosclerosis.

Ingredients:
- 16 ounces of eggplant
- 2 tablespoons of soy sauce
- 1/4 teaspoon of salt
- 2 cups of vegetable oil
- 1 tablespoon of cornstarch
- 1/2 tablespoon of ginger strips
- 1/2 tablespoon of green-onion chips
- 1/2 teaspoon of garlic chips
- 6 ounces of warm water

Directions:
1. Wash and peel eggplant; then cut into half-inch slices.
2. Heat vegetable oil in wok over high heat; then slide in eggplant and deep-fry until golden. Remove eggplant from wok, drain off oil, and let stand.
3. Make sauce by mixing soy sauce, ginger, green-onion chips, and cornstarch with 6 ounces of warm water.
4. Remove all but two tablespoons of oil from wok and turn on high heat.
5. Add in garlic chips and stir-fry for 10 seconds.
6. Put mixed sauce and eggplant into wok. Stir-fry for 2 minutes.
7. Remove and serve.

Wok Fried Turnips

Medicinal Uses:
Promotes a balanced metabolism.
Improves the appetite.
Improves digestion, especially for oily food.
Soothes qi.
Eliminates congestion.
Relieves asthma.
Helps to regulate urination.
Quenches thirst due to deficiency.
Used to treat indigestion, an inflated belly, a cough with congestion, chest congestion, and the flu.

Ingredients:

- 2 *cups of turnips*
- 2 *teaspoons of soy sauce*
- 1/4 *teaspoon of salt*
- 2 *tablespoons vegetable oil (divided in half)*
- 2 *tablespoons of cornstarch*
- 1/2 *tablespoon of ginger strips*
- 1/2 *tablespoon of green-onion chips*
- 1/2 *teaspoon of garlic chips*

Directions:

1. Wash and slice turnips into thick strips.
2. Heat 1 tablespoon of oil in wok over high heat; then slide in turnip strips, and stir-fry for 3 minutes. Remove from wok and let stand.
3. In a bowl make the sauce by mixing soy sauce, salt, starch, ginger strips, green-onion chips, and garlic chips. Fill bowl halfway with water and mix.
4. Heat remaining 1 tablespoon of oil over high heat. Put in mixed sauce and turnip strips in at the same time and stir-fry for 3 minutes.
5. Remove and serve.

White-gourd Sauté

Medicinal Uses:

Promotes the circulation of body fluid to improve urination.
Nourishes the liver.
Purges excessive body heat.
Harmonizes the stomach to adjust vital energy.
Used to treat hypertension, obesity, constipation, and liver disease.

Ingredients:

1.5 *pounds of white gourd*

2 *tablespoons of soy sauce*

1/4 *teaspoon of salt*

4 *tablespoons of vegetable oil*

2 *tablespoons of cornstarch*

Directions:

1. Peel white gourd and cut into 1-inch x 1-inch cubes.
2. Dissolve starch in 1/2 cup of water.
3. Put white-gourd cubes in boiling water for 3 minutes, until they look transparent. Remove, drain, and let cool.
4. Heat vegetable oil in wok over high heat; then add in soy sauce, salt, and 2 cups of water.
5. When the sauce boils, slide in white-gourd cubes and reduce to low heat. Simmer for 5 minutes.
6. Increase to high heat. Add cornstarch dissolved in water and stir for 30 seconds to make sauce thicker.
7. Transfer and serve.

Rice and Noodle Dishes

Steamed Rice

Ingredients:
  Measured rice
  Measured water

Directions:
  1. Put the desired amount of rice in a bowl.
  2. Pour water into the bowl until the water surface is 1 finger higher than the rice.
  3. Put the bowl in a pressure cooker and pour water into the pot.*
  4. Do not let water float the bowl.
  5. Put the pressure pot on your stove.
  6. Set heat to the maximum until you can hear the water boiling in the pot; then turn down the heat to medium.
  7. Allow rice to cook for 12–13 minutes.
  8. Turn off the heat and remove the pot; open the pot and carefully remove the bowl.

Note: *A pressure cooker is called for in this recipe because it cooks rice quickly. However rice can also be cooked in a saucepan with a tightly fitting lid according to the package directions.

Boiled Rice

Ingredients:
  Measured rice
  Measured water

Directions:
  1. Put the desired amount of rice in a regular pot (or pressure cooker).
  2. Pour water into the pot. If you are using a regular pot the water surface should be 1.5 fingers above the rice. If you are using a pressure cooker the water should be 1 finger above the rice.
  3. Put covered pot on the range top.
  4. For a regular pot, keep the heat at a medium temperature until no water is above the rice, and then switch heat to low.
  5. For a pressure pot, set the heat to maximum and when the vent nozzle stops spraying turn the heat down to medium.
  6. Rotate the pot so that each section gets cooked evenly.
  7. Remove pot from heat. Keep pot covered for at least one minute.

White Rice Congee

Medicinal Uses:
Used to treat weak stomachs and heart disease.
An ideal dish for those on a diet.

Ingredients:

1 cup white rice
8 1/2 cups of water

Directions:
1. Rinse rice lightly.
2. Put 1 cup of rice and 8 1/2 cups of water in a regular pot (or pressure cooker).
3. Put covered pot on the range top.
4. For a regular pot, keep the heat at a medium temperature for about 5 minutes, and then switch heat to low and simmer for 25 to 30 minutes.
5. For a pressure pot, set the heat to maximum and when the vent nozzle stops spraying turn the heat down to medium and simmer for 20 minutes.
6. Rotate the pot so that each section gets cooked evenly.
7. Remove pot from heat. Keep pot covered for at least one minute.

Fortune Fried Rice

Medicinal Uses:
Balances nutrition.
Replenishes protein.
Relieves constipation.
Lubricates the intestines.
Useful for treating diabetes.

Ingredients:

14 *ounces of cooked white rice*
3 *ounces of lean cooked pork*
1 *ounce of bamboo shoots*
1 *ounce of snow peas*
1 *ounce of thinly sliced carrots*
0.8 *ounce of soaked dried mushrooms*
2 *eggs*
2 *tablespoons of cooking wine*
1 *teaspoon of salt (divided in half)*
2 *ounces of olive oil*
1 *teaspoon of green-onion chips*
1/2 *cup of water*

Directions:

1. Cut mushrooms, cooked pork, and bamboo shoots into 1/4-inch cubes.
2. Beat the egg in a bowl; then add in green-onion chips and 1/2 teaspoon of salt. Mix well.
3. Heat 1 tablespoon of olive oil over medium heat, slide in egg mixture and cook for 30 seconds. Transfer to a bowl.
4. Heat remaining olive oil over high heat. Slide in mushrooms, pork, bamboo shoots, snow peas and carrot slices. Stir-fry for 5 minutes.
5. Add in cooking wine, the remaining 1/2 teaspoon of salt and half a cup of water.
6. Continue stir-frying for 3 minutes.
7. Add in white rice and egg and stir-fry for 6 minutes.
8. Sprinkle on green-onion chips and stir several times.
9. Remove and serve.

Scallop Fried Rice

Medicinal Uses:
Replenishes protein and vitamins.
Nourishes the kidneys and brain.
Improves vision.
Used to treat hypertension, diabetes, and obesity.

Ingredients:

20 *ounces of cooked white rice*

1.5 *ounces of scallops*

1.5 *ounces of Asparagus lettuce*

2 *eggs*

1/3 *tablespoon of salt of salt*

1/2 *teaspoon of pepper*

2 *tablespoons of olive oil*

2 *tablespoons of soy sauce*

Directions:

1. Cut scallops and Asparagus lettuce into half-inch cubes.
2. Hard boil eggs. Remove their shells and cut them into 6 pieces.
3. Heat oil in wok over high heat. Add in cooked white rice and stir-fry for 10 minutes until hot.
4. Slide in scallops, Asparagus lettuce, and eggs and stir-fry for 5 minutes.
5. Add in salt, pepper, and soy sauce. Go on stir-frying for another 2 minutes.
6. Remove and serve.

Vegetable Fried Rice

Medicinal Uses:

Is good for lubricating intestines.

Improves the digestion.

Used to treat hypertension, diabetes, obesity, cancer, and high cholesterol.

Ingredients:

3	ounces of white rice
1	ounce of onion
1	ounce of vegetable oil
1.2	ounces of soaked dried mushrooms
0.6	ounce of snow peas
0.6	ounce of carrot
1/4	teaspoon of salt
2	tablespoons of soy sauce
7	ounces of water
0.4	ounce of green pepper

Directions:

1. Wash white rice and drain.
2. Wash green pepper and boil in water. Remove pepper and cut into small pieces.
3. Cut onion, carrot, and soaked mushroom into small pieces.
4. Heat vegetable oil over medium heat. Slide in onion and carrot pieces and stir-fry for 3 minutes.
5. Add white rice; then pour in water until the water level is 1/2 finger higher than rice. Cover wok to boil for 20 minutes.
6. Remove the cover; then add mushrooms, green pepper, snow peas, and soy sauce.
7. Mix well and reduce to low heat to cook for another 5 minutes.
8. Remove and serve.

Note: Onion can cause gas and bloating in sensitive people.

Stewed Lamb Rice

Medicinal Uses:

A good summer food.

The combinations in this dish decrease the calories in the lamb.

Useful for treating hypertension, heart disease, and diabetes.

Ingredients:

2   *ounces of leg of Lamb*

1.5 *ounces of white rice*

2   *cloves of garlic*

9   *ounces of green onion (white part only)*

1.5 *ounces of snow peas*

3   *ounces of celery*

1/2 *teaspoon of ginger strips*

5   *pieces of dried red pepper*

4   *teaspoons of cooking wine*

2   *teaspoons of salt (divided in half)*

2   *teaspoons of soy sauce*

1   *teaspoon of pepper*

3   *ounces of peanut oil*

Directions:

1. Cut lamb meat into 1-inch cubes and put in a bowl.
2. Rub lamb with 1 teaspoon of salt and 1 teaspoon of pepper and allow to stand for 1/2 hour.
3. Cut green onion, celery, ginger, garlic and red pepper into small chips.
4. Heat peanut oil over high heat, slide in the lamb cubes, and deep-fry until they turn golden.
5. Remove lamb and drain off excess oil.
6. Leave half of the oil in the wok. Add in ginger, green onion, celery, dried red pepper and lamb.
7. Add 2 cups of water and bring to a boil.
8. Add cooking wine, the remaining salt, and 2 teaspoons soy sauce.
9. Reduce heat to low and cook 10 minutes.
10. Add in white rice and snow peas. Mix well.
11. Pour in just enough water to immerse the mixture.
12. Reduce heat to low and stew for 20 minutes.
13. Remove and serve.

Cold Noodles

Medicinal Uses:
Clears away excessive heat from the body.
Nourishes the stomach and spleen.
Replenishes protein.
Used to treat poor appetite and indigestion.

Ingredients:
0.8 *pound of noodles*
  3 *ounces of bean sprouts*
  1 *tablespoon of green-onion chips*
1/2 *tablespoon of ginger juice*
  2 *tablespoons of soy sauce*
1/2 *tablespoon of vinegar*
  1 *tablespoon of sesame paste*
1/2 *teaspoon of hot sauce*
  1 *tablespoon of sesame oil*
  2 *teaspoons of sesame seeds*
1/2 *teaspoon of garlic chips*

Directions:
1. Boil noodles until tender. Drain, set aside, and allow to cool.
2. Boil bean sprouts in water for 1 minute. Remove and drain.
3. Dry-fry sesame seeds in a pan until done; then grind it into powder while hot.
4. Squeeze the ginger to get its juice.
5. Make sauce by combining green-onion chips, ginger juice, garlic chips, sesame powder, soy sauce, vinegar, sesame paste, and hot pepper in a bowl and mixing well.
6. Put bean sprouts over the noodles and sprinkle on the mixed sauce.
7. Sprinkle on sesame oil and serve.

Pork Chow Mein

Medicinal Uses:

Nourishes intestines.

Protects blood vessels.

Cleans the intestines.

Used to treat arteriosclerosis and indigestion.

Ingredients:

3   *ounces of noodles*

2   *ounces of lean pork*

1.5   *ounces of spinach*

2   *tablespoons of vegetable oil (divided in half)*

1   *teaspoon of green-onion chips*

1   *teaspoon of salt*

Directions:

1. Cut pork into 2-inch-thick strips.
2. Wash spinach and cut into 1-inch strips.
3. Cook noodles in boiling water until tender. Remove and drain.
4. Heat 1 tablespoon of vegetable oil in wok over medium heat; then slide in pork strips and stir-fry for 3 minutes. Remove pork.
5. Add remaining oil to wok and add in noodles to stir-fry for 4 minutes.
6. Combine salt, pork strips, green-onion chips, and spinach and stir-fry for another 3 minutes.
7. Remove and serve.

Chicken Chow Mein

Medicinal Uses:
Replenishes normal protein and vitamins.
Restores energy.
Used to treat hypertension and high cholesterol.

Ingredients:

6	*ounces of noodles*
4	*ounces of chicken white meat*
2	*eggs*
2	*ounces of bean sprouts*
16	*ounces of olive oil*
1	*teaspoon of ginger strips*
1	*teaspoon of green-onion chips*
2	*teaspoons of salt (divided in half)*
1/2	*tablespoon of cornstarch*
1/2	*pound chicken (or pork) broth*

Directions:

1. Cut chicken into thin match-stick size strips.
2. Cut ginger and green onion into half-inch strips.
3. Remove egg yolks and whip egg whites.
4. Put chicken strips in a bowl, combine 1 teaspoon of salt, egg whites and cornstarch. Mix well and let stand.
5. Heat olive oil in wok over medium heat; then slide in chicken strips and deep-fry until they turn white. Transfer and drain.
6. Leave about 2 tablespoons of olive oil in wok; then slide in ginger and green-onion strips and stir-fry for 15 minutes.
7. Add in bean sprouts and stir-fry for 3 minutes.
8. Put in remaining salt and chicken broth. Bring to a boil. Transfer to a large bowl.
9. Cook noodles until done. Drain and transfer to a plate to let cool down.
10. Put 1 tablespoon olive oil in wok; add the noodles when oil gets hot.
11. Stir-fry till noodles turn golden on both sides.
12. Pour in soup, cover wok, and simmer for 5 minutes.
13. Add in chicken strips and mix well.
14. Remove and serve.

Steamed Spinach Noodles

Medicinal Uses:

Nourishes intestines.
Protects blood vessels.
Cleans the intestines.
Used to treat arteriosclerosis, hypertension, cancer, and indigestion.

Ingredients:

1   *pound of noodles*

1.5 *ounces of spinach*

1   *ounce of sesame oil*

1/3 *teaspoon of salt*

10   *ounces of chicken (or pork) broth*

Directions:

1. Cook noodles until done. Transfer and let stand.
2. Wash spinach and cut into 2-inch strips.
3. Combine chicken broth and salt and mix well.
4. Add in noodles and spinach strips.
5. Put the bowl in a steamer (or a large pot with water) to steam for 10 minutes.
6. Remove the bowl and sprinkle with sesame oil to serve.

Noodles With Tomato and Pork Toppings

Medicinal Uses:
Promotes the circulation of body fluid.
Improves urine flow.
Relieves swelling.
Used to treat hyperplasia of the prostate.

Ingredients:

1/2   *pound of noodles*

1.5   *ounces of pork*

4   *ounces of tomato*

2   *tablespoons of olive oil*

1   *teaspoon of green-onion chips*

1   *teaspoon of ginger strips*

1   *teaspoon of salt*

32   *ounces of chicken (or pork) broth*

Directions:

1. Cut pork into thin match-size strips.
2. Boil tomatoes in water until peels become soft. Remove peels and cut tomatoes into thick pieces.
3. Cut ginger and green onion into thin match-size strips.
4. Heat olive oil in wok, then slide in pork strips, ginger and green-onion strips and stir-fry for 3 minutes.
5. Pour in chicken broth and cook till boiling.
6. Put noodles in the wok to boil for 9 minutes.
7. Put in tomato pieces and add salt.
8. When it boils again, remove and serve.

Desserts

Banana With Juice

Medicinal Uses:

Calms the liver.
Removes excessive heat from the body.
Used to treat headache, dizziness, and tinnitus caused by hypertension.
Improves quality of sleep.

Ingredients:

20   *ounces of banana*

1.5 *ounce corncob*

16   *ounces of watermelon peel*

8   *ounces of raw sugar (divided in half)*

1   *ounce of Hawthorne*

Directions:

1. Peel bananas and cut into thick pieces.
2. Combine banana pieces with 4 ounces of raw sugar in a bowl.
3. Cover the bowl with a piece of wet etamine or cheesecloth and steam for half an hour.
4. Cut watermelon peel into small pieces.
5. Pour 1/4 gallon of water into a pot. Add watermelon peels, corncob, and Hawthorne into the pot and steam over high heat for 20 minutes.
6. Takes 1 1/4 cups of mixed juice from the pot and filter it through the etamine or cheesecloth.
7. Stir remaining raw sugar into the mixed juice, and pour the mixture over the steamed banana in the bowl.
8. Serve.

Watermelon Congee

Medicinal Uses: ✳

Removes summer heat.

Calms the mind.

Stimulates urination.

Reduces swelling due to kidney disorders, diabetes, and choleplania. It is an ideal food in the summer and for those who work in high-temperature environments.

Ingredients:

8   *ounces of watermelon peel*

4   *ounces of white rice*

1.5   *ounces of raw sugar*

Directions:

1. Wash watermelon peel and rice.
2. Cut watermelon peel into 5 pieces.
3. Put rice into a pot and pour in 1/4 gallon of water. Heat over medium heat until it boils.
4. Reduce to a low heat and stew for another 30 minutes.
5. Put in watermelon peels and simmer for another 15 minutes.
6. Remove and discard watermelon peels.
7. Add in raw sugar and mix well.
8. Remove and serve.

Lotus Leaf Congee

Medicinal Uses:

Clears excessive heat from the body.
Invigorates yang of the spleen.
Dissolves stasis to stop bleeding.
Is used to treat sunstroke and dizziness in the summer.
Used to treat hypertension, high blood fat, and obesity.

Ingredients:

1 *piece of fresh lotus leaf*

3 *ounces of rice*

1.5 *ounces of raw sugar*

Directions:

1. Wash lotus leaf and rice.
2. Cut lotus leaf into 4 large pieces.
3. Put rice into a pot, pour in 1/4 gallon of water, and keep on medium heat until it boils.
4. Reduce to low heat and stew for another 30 minutes.
5. Stir in lotus leave pieces and go on simmering for another 15 minutes.
6. Remove and discard leaves.
7. Add raw sugar and mix well.
8. Remove and serve.

Pear Congee

Medicinal Uses:

Clears away excessive heat to stop a cough.

Promotes the production of body fluid to quench one's thirst.

Protects the throat.

Serves as an ideal food for singers, broadcasters and teachers.

Ingredients:

3 *pears*

3 *ounces of rice*

2 *ounces of raw sugar*

Directions:

1. Wash pears and rice.
2. Peel pears and cut them into small chunks (discard the cores).
3. Bring 1/4 gallon of water to a boil over medium heat.
4. Add in pears. Reduce to a low heat and simmer for 30 minutes, until fluid becomes very thick.
5. Add in raw sugar and stir until it melts.
6. Remove and serve.

Tremella (White-tree-fungi) Soup

Medicinal Uses:

Nourishes yin and the stomach.

Produces body fluid

Regulates the blood.

Is especially good as supplement food for patients with a sustained low fever.

Ingredients:

0.35 *ounce of tremella*

2 *tablespoons of raw sugar.*

Directions:

1. Wash the tremella to remove dirt.
2. Soak it in 1.5 bowls of cold water for one day. The tremella will become swollen and transparent.
3. Pour the tremella together with the soaking water into a steel pot.
4. Add raw sugar
5. Simmer over low heat for at least 1 hour until the tremella turns soft.
6. Serve.

Date and Lotus Seed Soup

Medicinal Uses:

Enhances the heart.

Invigorates the spleen.

Calms the mind.

Stabilizes the blood pressure and promotes blood circulation.

Improves heart functions.

Improves the appetite.

Helps improve sleep quality.

Ingredients:

7 *dates*

1.8 *ounces of lotus seeds*

1/2 *tablespoon of sugar*

Directions:

1. Soak dates in warm water for about 5 minutes. Wash and drain.
2. Soak lotus seeds in hot water until they swell.
3. Put the lotus seeds in a steel pot, add 2 large bowls of water and bring to a boil over high heat.
4. When boiling, reduce heat to low and simmer for 1 hour.
5. Add dates and sugar to stew for another 30 minutes (or till lotus seeds and dates turn soft).

Lotus-seed Pudding

Medicinal Uses:
Nourishes the kidneys.
Invigorates the spleen.
Nourishes the heart.
Calms the mind.
Helps combat fatigue.
Stimulates a poor appetite.
Relieves men's loin pain due to excessive seminal emission
Used to treat women's excessive discharge.
Serves as an ideal food for office workers and young couples.
Acts as a cancer preventive.

Ingredients:

2 *ounces of white lotus seeds*
0.035 *ounce of ginseng*
0.18 *ounce of Red China dates*
1 *ounce of raw sugar*

Directions:

1. Wash lotus seeds with cold water and red dates with warm water.
2. Put lotus seeds, ginseng, and red dates in a bowl. Pour in 1/4 gallon of water.
3. Cover the bowl and put it into a pot with water.
4. Put the pot on low heat to steam for 2 hours.
5. Put raw sugar in the bowl. Cover the bowl and steam for another hour, until the lotus seeds become very tender.

Papaya and Coix-seed Soup

Medicinal Uses:

Nourishes the liver.

Acts as a muscle relaxer.

Alleviates water retention and swelling.

Regulates the stomach.

Relieves abdominal distension.

Is effective in treating ankle and knee-joint pains.

Ingredients:

0.35   *ounce of papaya*

1   *ounce of coix seed**

1   *tablespoon of raw sugar*

Directions:

1. Put clean papaya and coix seeds into a steel pot and add one and one half big bowls of water.
2. Soak for 10 minutes.
3. Put the pot over low heat and simmer till coix seeds begin to melt.
4. Add raw sugar and simmer for another 10 minutes.
5. Serve.

Note: Coix seeds, often called Job's Tears in the United States, are a cereal grain grown in central and southern Asia. You can purchases the seeds in any Chinese grocery store.

Lotus-seeds Congee

Medicinal Uses:
Invigorates the kidney.
Nourishes the heart.
Cleans the intestines.
Treats loose bowels caused by a spleen deficiency.
Fights excessive seminal emission due to kidney deficiency.
Reduces frequent urination at night.
Treats night sweats.

Ingredients:
1.5 ounces of white lotus seeds
3 ounces of sticky rice
1.6 ounces of brown sugar

Directions:
1. Wash lotus seeds and crush them into large pieces.
2. Wash sticky rice.
3. Put sticky rice and lotus seeds in a pot. Pour in 1/4 gallon of water.
4. Pot the pot on medium heat and cook until it boils.
5. Reduce heat to low and simmer for 30 minutes until the soup becomes thick.
6. Add in brown sugar.
7. Mix well and serve.

Chinese Yam With Black Sesame Seeds

Medicinal Uses:
Invigorates the spleen and stomach.
Nourishes the lungs and kidneys.
Used for fatigue.
Treats poor appetite due to hypofunction of the spleen.
Helpful for cough and asthma due to lung deficiency.
Is used to treat problematic seminal emission and frequent urination due to kidney deficiency.

Ingredients:

10	*ounces of Chinese yam*
1/2	*ounce of black sesame seeds**
4	*ounces of raw sugar*
3	*ounces of vegetable oil*
1	*cup of water*

Directions:
1. Wash black sesame seeds. Dry-fry 10 minutes, until you can smell the fragrance.
2. Peel Chinese yam and cut into half-inch-thick pieces.
3. Heat vegetable oil in wok over medium. Slide in yam pieces and deep-fry until they float (they will be crisp on the surface and tender inside).
4. Transfer yams to a plate and let stand.
5. Remove oil from wok and replace with sugar and a cup of water. Stir-fry quickly until the sugar melts.
6. Push in yam pieces and stir continuously until they are coated completely with sugar.
7. Remove yam pieces.
8. Sprinkle on black sesame seeds and serve.

Note: *Black sesame seeds are stronger in aroma and flavor than white sesame seeds. They can be purchased in any Chinese grocery store as well as many Japanese and Indian groceries.

Chinese-yam Congee

Medicinal Uses: ✳

Strengthens the spleen.

Nourishes the stomach and kidneys.

Invigorates the lungs.

Stimulates the appetite.

Treats loose bowels caused by deficiencies of the spleen and the stomach.

Used to treat malnourished children.

Aids against abnormal female discharge.

Reduces a cough due to deficiency of the lung.

Used to treat trouble with seminal emission and enuresis due to deficiency of the kidney.

Helpful for chronic gastritis.

Ingredients:

4   *ounces of fresh yams*

4   *ounces of sticky rice*

2.5   *ounces of raw sugar*

Directions:

1. Peel the yams and cut into 1 inch cubes.
2. Wash sticky rice.
3. Put yam cubes and sticky rice in a pot and pour in 1/4 gallon of water. Cook over medium heat until boiling.
4. Reduce to low heat and simmer for 1 hour, until the fluid inside the pot become very thick.
5. Add in raw sugar and mix well and serve.

White-fungus Congee

Medicinal Uses:
   Restores yin.
   Lubricates the lungs.
   Promotes the production of body fluid.
   Nourishes the stomach.
   Used to treat an unproductive cough, blood in the phlegm, and constipation.

Ingredients:
   0.3 *ounce of white fungus*
   2 *pounds of rice*
   5 *red dates*
   1.5 *ounces of raw sugar*

Directions:
   1. Soak white fungus in hot water until it swells.
   2. Clean fungus carefully to remove dirt.
   3. Clean rice and red dates.
   4. Put white fungus and dates in a pot. Pour in 1/4 gallon of water.
   5. Put the pot over medium heat until it boils.
   6. Reduce to low heat and cook for about 45 minutes, until fluid in the pot becomes very thick.
   7. Add in raw sugar and simmer for another 5 minutes.
   8. Serve.

Honey Walnut Kernel

Medicinal Uses:
Nourishes the kidney to restrict seminal emission.
Calms asthma and coughs due to kidney deficiency.
Counteracts constipation due to intestinal dryness.
Used to treat senior bronchitis and constipation.

Ingredients:

> 20 *ounces of fresh walnut kernels*
> 6 *ounces of honey*
> 2 *ounces of raw sugar*
> 1 *ounce of red cherries*
> 1 *ounce of tangerine sections*

Directions:

1. Soak the walnut kernels in boiling water and remove any excess skin. Put them in a bowl.
2. Add raw sugar and put the bowl in a pot with water to steam for 15 minutes.
3. Put steamed walnut kernels on a plate (reserving the juice that resulted from steaming separately). Place tangerine sections and cherries over the kernels.
4. Put a pan over low heat and add in honey. Cook until boiling. Pour in the kernel juice and mix well.
5. Pour the mixture of honey and kernel juice over the walnut kernels.
6. Serve.

Lotus-root Congee

Medicinal Uses:
Invigorates the spleen.
Stimulates the appetite.
Replenishes the blood.
Reverses diarrhea.
Used to treat fatigue, poor appetite and loose bowels due to under-functioning of the spleen and stomach, as well as thirst during recovery period after an illness.

Ingredients:
9   *ounces of fresh lotus root*
3   *ounces of sticky rice*
1.5   *ounces of brown sugar*

Directions:
1. Shave the lotus root's surface.
2. Cut the lotus root into half-inch cubes.
3. Wash sticky rice.
4. Put lotus-root cubes and sticky rice together in a soup pot. Pour in 1/4 gallon of water.
5. Cook over medium heat until boiling. Reduce heat to low and simmer for nearly 1 hour until the fluid inside becomes very thick.
6. Add brown sugar and mix well.
7. Serve.

Wolfberry-fruit Congee

Medicinal Uses:
Nourishes the kidneys.
Replenishes the blood.
Nourishes yin.
Improves vision.
Can be used to treat weakness in the loins and knees.
Treats dizziness.
Fights deficiencies of the liver and kidney.

Ingredients:
1.5 ounces of Wolfberry fruit*
1/2 cup of rice
1.5 ounces of raw sugar

Directions:
1. Wash wolfberry fruit and rice.
2. Put them in a soup pot and pour in 1/4 gallon of water. Cook over medium heat till boiling.
3. Reduce to low heat and simmer for another 40 minutes, until the fluid becomes very thick.
4. Add in sugar and mix well.
5. Serve.

Note: *Wolfberry fruit are the bright red, sweet, berries of a woody shrub that is native to China and Tibet. The Wolfberry fruit, also known as Lycium, can be found in any Chinese grocery store.

PART THREE:
Sample
Diet Plans

CHAPTER 6
Sample Diet Plans

Food and Common Illnesses

AILMENT

Fever

Foods to Eat

Plain foods. Noodles, rice, fresh vegetables, sugar cane, oranges, and other fresh fruits.

Foods to Avoid

Oily, deep-fried, and pungent foods.

AILMENT

Chronic bronchitis

Foods to Eat

Plain and easily digested, high-calorie and high-vitamin foods. Eel, soft-shelled turtle, kelp, radishes, water chestnuts, and fresh greens.

Foods to Avoid

Alcohol, smoked, oily and pungent foods.

AILMENT

Hyperlipemia, hypertension, and coronary diseases

Foods to Eat

Plain foods. Rice, wheat flour, corn., fresh greens, beans, melons, kelp. Vegetable oil.

Water chestnuts, hawthorn, persimmon, and bee honey

Foods to Avoid

High-fat, high-cholesterol and pungent foods. Fat meat, animal fat and organs, egg yolk, roe. Alcohol, strong tea, and coffee.

AILMENT

Liver diseases

Foods to Eat

Acute hepatitis: plain foods. Moderate amounts of milk, eggs, fish, beans and bean products like tofu and soy-milk. Sugar, jam, honey and other high calorie foods. Vegetables with strong vitamin content such as greens, bean sprouts, tomatoes, and various melons.

Chronic hepatitis: fresh vegetables, tofu, jam, fish and sweet congees (rice porridges).

Foods to Avoid

Pungent foods. Alcohol. Minimize salt intake. Beans, potatoes, and sweet potatoes.

Cholecystitis and choleithiasis

Foods to Eat

Fresh vegetables like greens, radishes and turnips. Edible wild herbs, tomatoes, and melons. Fresh fruits.

Foods to Avoid

High-cholesterol, fat, deep-fried, and pungent foods.

Stomach diseases

Foods to Eat

Acute gastritis: In the beginning limit yourself to only liquid or half-liquid foods like vegetable and fruit juices. Easy-digested foods can then be added

Chronic gastritis: Easily digested foods with high vitamin B, protein, and iron.

Gastroduodenal ulcer: Easily digested food such as congees, bean products, and greens.

Ptosis of the stomach: nutritious but easily digested foods such as sticky-rice, congee, eggs, milk, lean meat, fish, chicken, pork liver, and greens.

Foods to Avoid

Alcohol, strong tea or coffee, pungent foods, deep-fried foods, cold; and hard foods

Diabetes

Foods to Eat

Low sugar fruits like kiwi and bananas. Low-starch foods. Fresh vegetables like cabbage, chives, radishes, tomatoes, and carrots.

Foods to Avoid

Sugar, jam, and honey. Large amounts of wheat flour, potatoes, and lotus roots.

Tuberculosis

Foods to Eat

High calorie foods rich in proteins, calcium, and vitamins such as meats, milk, eggs, fish, fresh vegetables and fruits. Goat milk.

Foods to Avoid

Alcohol. Smoked, oily and pungent foods.

Anemia

Foods to Eat

Foods with high iron content. Some animal organs like liver. Lean meats, eggs, milk, soybeans. Vegetables especially spinach and tomatoes. Fruits like pineapples, dates, apricots, peaches, oranges, and tangerines.

Foods to Avoid

None

AILMENT

Chronic constipation

Foods to Eat

Fresh fruits like pears and apples. Fresh vegetables like celery. Foods that can create gas such as onions, soybeans, and radishes. Plenty of water.

Foods to Avoid

Pungent and hot foods.

AILMENT

Kidney diseases

Foods to Eat

Acute kidney disorders: sugar congees, vegetables, fruits, jams, and honey. Low salt foods and high protein foods.

Chronic kidney disorders: low salt foods, easily digested foods. Fruits. Vegetables like white gourd, squash, bamboo shoots, greens, and radishes.

Foods to Avoid

Greasy foods, deep-fried and cold foods. Garlic, scallions, chives and hot peppers. Alcohol.

AILMENT

Skin diseases

Foods to Eat

Towel gourd. Plain foods.

Foods to Avoid

Yellow fish, crab, shrimp, mushrooms, bamboo shoots, and chives.

AILMENT

Cancer

Foods to Eat

Skin cancer, matrix cancer, prostate cancer, breast cancer: plain foods. Vegetables, fruits, nuts, and seeds.

Liver cancer, lung cancer, stomach cancer: Vegetarian foods, organic foods, nuts and seeds.

Foods to Avoid

Seafood, mushrooms, bamboo shoots and chives. All pungent foods.

AILMENT

Arthritis

Foods to Eat

Moderately pungent foods like ginger and hot pepper.

Foods to Avoid

Eggplant, tomato, and potatoes.

Alzheimer's

Foods to Eat

Eat less to accelerate toxic discharge from the body. Do fasting and exercise.

Foods to Avoid

None

Hypertension

Keeping your blood pressure under control is tremendously important to your overall health. High blood pressure is one of several factors associated with cardiovascular disease, which is the number 1 killer of United States citizens...both men and women. Cardiovascular disease claims more lives annually than all cancers combined, killing approximately 1 million people in the United States each year. It disables countless others.

The cause of high blood pressure is unknown in 90 percent of all cases. This is called "essential hypertension." In secondary hypertension, a disease or other physical problem is behind the diagnosis. Common causes are kidney disease and thyroid disease. Many factors are associated with high blood pressure, including genetics, age, race, stress, obesity, smoking, a high-salt diet, excessive consumption of alcohol, and a sedentary lifestyle.

High blood pressure can develop over many years with no noticeable symptoms. Warning signs can include nosebleeds, a racing or an irregular heartbeat, headaches, and dizziness.

*Important: Please note that certain recipes indicated as good choices for those who suffer from hypertension may have salt included in them. If you suffer from high blood pressure you can eliminate the salt from a recipe and substitute an alternative spice.

To control blood pressure, you should do the following:

- Have your blood pressure checked regularly. Your primary care physician can tell you how often.
- Stop smoking.
- Avoid excessive salt intake. Excessive salt can make high blood pressure worse. It causes water retention, which makes your heart work harder than it has to. The National High Blood Pressure Education Program recommends no more than 2,400 milligrams per day (the amount in about 1 teaspoon of table salt).
- Eat more fresh fruits, vegetables, and foods high in fiber...and less fat. High-fiber foods also include tofu and other bean products. Seafood (except some with high cholesterol, such as shrimp and crab), chicken, and duck are also acceptable.
- Reduce stress on and off the job; master relaxation techniques.
- Be moderate in your drinking.
- Exercise regularly, and keep your weight within normal limits.
- If your doctor prescribes medication to lower your blood pressure, be sure to follow his or her directions exactly.

Suggested foods for hypertension:

Breakfast: Oatmeal or grits, soymilk, yogurt, tea, low-fat or fat-free milk, fruit

Lunch: vegetable or fruit salad, nuts, rice, vegetables, noodles, bean products, fish, chicken

Dinner: Bean products, fish, vegetables, soups, chicken, fish, beef, lamb, and pork

Master Hou's Advice:

1. Eat meat no more than three times a week.
2. Eat more than 1.5 pounds of vegetables and more than 1 pound of fruit each day.
3. Eat plant proteins when possible (such as mushrooms, wheat flour, and soybean products).
4. Drink more tea especially herb teas.
5. Drink more than 6 glasses of carrot juice each week.
6. Try to eat only well done meats and avoid rare meats.
7. Fish should not be eaten more than 3 times a week.

Follow this plan for two months. Please note that dishes and beverages can be varied based on the general principles above. This plan is provided as a guideline. Corresponding page numbers are provided for the specific recipes mentioned in the book.

MONDAY

Breakfast

1. Oatmeal or grits..1 bowl
2. Sweet and Sour Cucumbers (183)..1 dish
3. Tea (Chrysanthemum Tea (51) or green tea)...........................1 cup
4. Whole wheat bread...1 slice

Lunch

1. Vegetable salad (may include chicken and nuts).......................1 dish
2. Whole wheat bread...1 slice
3. Tea (Chrysanthemum Tea (51) or green tea)...........................1 cup

Dinner

1. Gingered Carp (154)..1 dish
2. Chinese Caggabge with Mushrooms (165)................................1 dish
3. Fruit (apple, orange, or banana)..1 piece

TUESDAY

Breakfast

1. Golden Fried Wheat Flour Tea (177)...1 dish
2. Orange juice or green tea..1 glass or cup
3. Fruit (apple, orange, or banana)..1 piece

Lunch

1. Steamed Spinach Noodles (243) ....1 dish
2. Vegetable salad ....1 dish

Dinner

1. Tofu with Minced Pork (110) ....1 dish
2. Mushroom with Garlic (169) ....1 dish
3. Fruit (orange, apple, banana, or kiwi) ....1 piece

WEDNESDAY

Breakfast

1. Oatmeal or grits..1 bowl
2. Bitter Melon with Soybeans (180) ....1 dish
3. Fresh carrot juice...1 glass

Lunch

1. Spicy Gingered Chicken (122) ....1 dish
2. Sandwich (chicken or tuna)...1 sandwich
3. Tea (lemon tea) ....1 cup

Dinner

1. Spinach and Pork Soup (82) ....1 bowl
2. Tofu with Green Onions (189) ....1 dish
3. String Beans in Ginger Juice (194) ....1 dish
4. Fruit (orange, apple, banana, or kiwi) ....1 piece

THURSDAY

Breakfast

1. Soy milk plus one egg white..1 glass
2. Cucumber with Coriander and Hot Green Pepper (185) ....1 dish
3. Whole wheat bread ....1 slice
3. Tea (Chrysanthemum Tea (51) or green tea) ....1 cup

Lunch

1. White Rice Congee (235) ....1 dish
2. Scallop Fried Rice (237) ....1 dish
3. Fruit (orange, apple, banana, or kiwi) ....1 piece

Dinner

1. Hot Green Pepper with Potato Strips (208) ....1 dish
2. Spicy Gingered Chicken (122) ....1 dish
3. Young Chinese Cabbage and Tofu Soup (88).........................1 bowl
4. Tea (Chrysanthemum Tea (51) or green tea) ....1 cup

FRIDAY

Breakfast

1. White Rice Congee (235) ....1 dish
2. Spiced-up Celery (190)...1 dish
3. Whole wheat bread ....1 cup
4. Tea (Chrysanthemum Tea (51) or green tea) ....1 cup

Lunch

1. Sandwich (chicken or tuna)..1 sandwich
2. Vegetable salad ....1 dish
3. Fresh carrot juice..1 glass

Dinner

1. Lamb with Carrots (100)...1 dish
2. Peanuts and Celery (204)..1 dish
3. White rice (or 1 slice of whole wheat bread).................................1 bowl
4. Bamboo Shoots and Tofu Soup (62)...1 bowl

SATURDAY

Breakfast

1. Oatmeal or grits...1 bowl
2. Spiced-up Celery (190)...1 dish

Lunch

1. Pork Chow Mein (241)..1 dish
2. Fruit (orange, apple, banana, or kiwi)...1 piece
3. Tea (Chrysanthemum Tea (51) or green tea) ....1 cup

Dinner

1. Jellyfish and Turnip (155) ....1 dish
2. Green Bell Pepper with Green Bean Sprouts (197)...........................1 dish
3. Soybean and Pork Spareribs Soup (81)..1 bowl
4. Tea (Chrysanthemum Tea (51) or green tea)....................................1 cup

SUNDAY

Breakfast & Lunch

1. Golden Fried Wheat Flour Tea (177) ....1 dish
2. Fruit Juice ....1 glass
3. Stewed Lamb Rice (239)...1 dish

Dinner

1. Tomato and Pork Soup (84) ....1 bowl
2. Vegetable salad ....1 dish
3. Fish Fillet with Cucumber (151) ....1 dish
4. Whole wheat bread ....2 pieces

Diabetes

According to the National Institute of Health 15.7 million Americans, almost 6 percent of the U.S. population, have diabetes. There are approximately 798,000 new cases diagnosed a year — and hundreds of thousands that go tragically undiagnosed.

Diabetes is a quiet killer that can cause serious health problems. It is the leading cause of adult blindness, kidney failure and non-traumatic amputations. Those suffering from diabetes have a 2 to 4 times higher risk of having a stroke or dieing from heart disease. And if you're a diabetic you have a 60 to 65 percent chance of having high blood pressure. So far there is no cure. Diabetes can be controlled, however, through diet, exercise, and medication.

When people eat, food is normally digested and much of it is converted to glucose — a simple sugar that the body uses for energy. The blood carries the glucose to cells, where it is absorbed with the help of the hormone insulin. For those with diabetes, however, the body does not make enough or cannot properly use the insulin it does make. Without insulin, glucose accumulates in the blood instead of moving into the cells. Thus, diabetes is the name for a group of disorders characterized by high blood-sugar levels.

There are two major types of diabetes: Type I, sometimes called juvenile onset or insulin-dependent diabetes, and Type II, often referred to as adult-onset or non-insulin-dependent diabetes.

Those with Type I diabetes must take insulin to utilize glucose and avoid ketoacidosis, a life-threatening condition occurring when the body burns fat for energy instead of glucose. Type I diabetes is more common in whites in other ethnic groups.

Type II diabetes is the most common in the United States, accounting for more than 90 percent of all cases. The risk factors of Type II include obesity, unfavorable body-fat distribution, and inactivity. People with Type II control their condition by limiting the type and amount of food they eat and by exercising. It is more common among Hispanics, Native-Americans, African-Americans, Alaskan natives, Pacific Islanders, and those of Asian ancestry than among Caucasians.

*Important: Please note that certain recipes indicated as good choices for those who suffer from diabetes may have sugar included in them. Diabetics should eliminate the sugar from the recipe or substitute an appropriate sweetener as recommended by their physician.

Suggested foods for diabetes:

Breakfast: Oatmeal or grits, soy-milk, low-fat or fat-free milk, fruit
Lunch: vegetables, fruit that is low in sugar, salad, nuts, rice, bean products, fish, chicken
Dinner: Bean products, fish, vegetables, soups, chicken, beef, lamb, and pork

Master Hou's advice:

- Eat foods that are low in sugar.
- Eat less wheat flour, as it contains a lot of starch that can be converted into sugar. Eat no more than three wheat-flour dishes per week and be sure each dish contains no more than 7 ounces of wheat flour.
- Rice, oatmeal and grits are acceptable foods.
- Meat and seafood in moderation are acceptable.
- Eat at least 2 pounds of vegetables a day. Vegetables like cauliflower, cabbage, and green pepper are ideal foods for diabetics.
- Eat lower sugar fruits, such as bananas and kiwis.
- Diabetics may feel hungry more often than other people. When hunger strikes try eating more vegetables.

Diet plan for a week

Follow this plan for two months. Please note that dishes and beverages can be varied based on the general principles above. This plan is provided as a guideline. Corresponding page numbers are provided for the specific recipes mentioned in the book.

MONDAY

Breakfast

1. Soy milk or fat-free milk ....1 glass
2. Spinach and Celery in Sesame Oil (191) ....1 dish
3. Tea (Chrysanthemum Tea (51) or green tea) ....1 cup

Lunch

1. Sweet and Sour Crisp-skin Crucian Fish (153) ....1 dish
2. Vegetable salad (may include chicken and nuts) ....1 dish

Dinner

1. Pork Spareribs with Kelp Soup (68) ....1 bowl
2. Stewed Lamb Rice (239) ....1 dish
3. Cucumber with Garlic (184) ....1 dish

TUESDAY

Breakfast

1. Soy milk or fat-free milk plus 1-2 egg whites..1 glass
2. Vegetable salad ....1 dish
3. Tea (Chrysanthemum Tea (51) or green tea) ....1 cup

Lunch

1. Pork with Asparagus Lettuce (97) ....1 dish
2. Chinese Cabbage with Mushrooms (165)..1 dish
3. Brown or white rice...1 bowl

Dinner

1. Tofu with Minced Pork (110)...1 dish
2. Mushroom with Garlic (169) ....1 dish
3. A low-sugar fruit (banana, kiwi, or avocado) ....1 piece

WEDNESDAY

Breakfast

1. Oatmeal or grits...1 bowl
2. Vegetable salad ....1 dish
3. Whole wheat bread ....1 piece

Lunch

1. Sandwich (chicken or tuna)...1 sandwich
2. Your choice of a vegetable..1 dish

Dinner

1. Inkfish with Chives (142)..1 dish
2. Stewed Lean Pork with Mushrooms (118)..1 dish
3. Towel Gourd with Pork Soup (85) ....1 bowl

THURSDAY

Breakfast

1. Soy milk plus one egg white...1 glass
2. Vegetable salad ....1 dish
3. Tea (Chrysanthemum Tea (51) or green tea) ....1 cup

Lunch

1. Brown or white rice...1 dish
2. Seared Beef with Turnip (95) ....1 dish
3. Crisp and Hot Cucumber Strips (175) 1dish

Dinner

1. Young Chinese Cabbage and Tofu Soup (88) ....1 bowl
2. Shrimp with Steamed Egg (128)..1 dish
3. Hot Green Pepper with Bitter melon (192)..1 dish
4. Chrysanthemum Tea (51) ....1 cup

FRIDAY

Breakfast

1. Soy milk plus one egg white...1 glass
2. Vegetable salad ....1 dish
3. Tea (Chrysanthemum Tea (51) or green tea) or black coffee..................1 cup

Lunch

1. Fortune Fried Rice (236) ....1 dish
2. Green Bell Pepper with Green Bean Sprouts (197)................................1 dish

Dinner

1. Sautéed Lamb (116)...1 dish
2. Hot Green Pepper with Bitter Melon (192)..1 dish
3. Delicious Dynasty Soup (65)..1 bowl
4. A low sugar fruit (banana, kiwi, or avocado) ....1 piece

SATURDAY

Breakfast

1. Soy milk plus one egg white...1 glass
2. Vegetable salad ....1 dish
3. A low sugar fruit (banana, kiwi, or avocado) ....1 piece
4. Tea (Chrysanthemum Tea (51) or green tea) or black coffee..................1 cup

Lunch

1. Sandwich (chicken or tuna)..1 sandwich
2. Bamboo shoots with Green Onions (210)..1 dish
3. Spicy Gingered Chicken (122) ....1 dish

Dinner

1. Eggplant Strips Sauté (219)..1 dish
2. Butterfish with Garlic (138) ....1 dish
3. Sesame Spinach (181)...1 dish

SUNDAY

Breakfast & Lunch

1. Mushroom and Snow Peas Soup (76)...1 bowl
2. Spicy Pork Strips with Squash (108)..1 dish
3. Brown or white rice...1 bowl

Dinner

1. Fresh corn with Hot Green Pepper (173) ....1 dish
2. Spiced-up Celery (190)...1 dish
3. Soybean and Pork Spareribs Soup (81)..1 bowl

Weight loss/Obesity

Over one-half of all Americans (about 97 million) are overweight or obese. If you are carrying this extra weight you are at risk for developing many diseases, including heart disease, stroke, diabetes, and cancer. Losing the extra weight helps to prevent and control those diseases. The following guidelines provide you with a new approach for safe and effective weight loss.

Suggested foods for weight reduction:
Breakfast: soy-milk, low-fat or fat-free milk, and fruit
Lunch: vegetable or low-sugar fruit salad, nuts, rice, bean products, fish, chicken
Dinner: Bean products, vegetables, soups, chicken, fish

Master Hou's advice:
- Follow a low calorie diet (LCD) for weight loss. Reducing fat as part of a LCD is a practical way to reduce calories.
- Reducing dietary fat alone without reducing calories is not sufficient for weight loss. However, reducing dietary fat, along with reducing dietary carbohydrates, can help reduce calories.
- Physical activity should be an integral part of weight loss therapy and weight maintenance.
- Daily vegetable consumption should not be less than 3 pounds. Eat only one meat dish a day.
- Eat high fiber foods, especially raw vegetables.
- Do not eat overeat at one meal.
- Drink water instead of other drinks.

Diet plan for a week:

Follow this plan for two months. Please note that dishes and beverages can be varied based on the general principles above. This plan is provided as a guideline. Corresponding page numbers are provided for the specific recipes mentioned in the book.

MONDAY

Breakfast
1. Soy milk plus two egg whites...1 glass
2. Vegetable salad ....1 dish
3. Green tea...1 cup

Lunch
1. Sandwich (chicken or tuna)...1 sandwich
2. Spiced-up Celery (190)...1 dish

Dinner
1. Green Bean Sprouts with Chives (198)...1 dish
2. Spicy Radishes (212) ....1 dish
3. Whole wheat bread ....1 slice

TUESDAY

Breakfast
1. Soy milk plus two egg whites..1 glass
2. A low-sugar fruit (banana or kiwi)...1 piece

Lunch
1. Vegetable Fried Rice (238) ....1 dish
2. Vegetable salad ....1 dish

Dinner
1. Tofu in Tomato Sauce (188) ....1 dish
2. Sweet and Sour Cucumbers (183) ....1 dish
3. Whole wheat bread ....2 slices

WEDNESDAY

Breakfast
1. Fat-free milk..1 glass
2. Vegetable salad ....1 dish

Lunch
1. Chinese Cabbage in Vinegar (163) ....1 dish
2. Shrimp with Cauliflower (131)..1 dish

Dinner
1. Wok-fried Tomatoes (168)...1 dish
2. Salty Shrimp (133)...1 dish
3. Chinese Broccoli Sauté (213) ....1 dish

THURSDAY

Breakfast
1. Soy milk plus one egg white..1 glass
2. Vegetable salad ....1 dish
3. Tea (Chrysanthemum Tea (51) or green tea............................1 cup

Lunch
1. Brown or white rice...1 bowl
2. Pork Strips with Celery and Carrot (111)................................1 dish
3. Cucumber with Garlic (184)...1 dish

Dinner
1. Turnips and Crushed Garlic (186) ....1 dish
2. Sour Noodle Soup (80)..1 dish
3. Vegetable salad ....1 dish
4. Chrysanthemum Tea (51)..1 cup

FRIDAY

Breakfast
1. Soy milk plus one egg white..1 glass
2. Avocado with Tomato (179) ....1 dish
3. Whole wheat bread ....1 slice

Lunch
1. Fish Fillet with Cucumber (151) ....1 dish
2. Spiced-up Celery (190)..1 dish
3. A low-sugar fruit (banana or kiwi)...1 piece

Dinner
1. Tofu in Tomato Sauce (188) ....1 dish
2. Pork Spareribs with Kelp Soup (68)...1 bowl
3. Bitter Melon in Red-Pepper Oil (193)......................................1 dish

SATURDAY

Breakfast
1. Soy milk plus one egg white..1 glass
2. Vegetable salad ....1 dish
3. A low-sugar fruit (banana or kiwi)...1 piece
4.Tea (Chrysanthemum Tea (51) or green) ....1 cup

Lunch
1. Sandwich (chicken or tuna)...1 sandwich
2. Spicy Gingered Chicken (122)...1 dish
3. Sweet and Sour Cucumbers (183)...1 dish

Dinner
1. Sautéed Conch-slices (152) ....1 dish
2. Spiced Turnip and Lamb Soup (86) ....1 bowl

3. Sesame Celery (178) ....1 dish
4. Brown or white rice...1 bowl

SUNDAY

Breakfast & Lunch
1. White-gourd Sauté (232) ....1 dish
2. Egg with Cucumber (174) ....1 dish
3. Whole wheat bread ....2 slices

Dinner
1. Eggplant Strips Sauté (219)...1 dish
2. Celery, Kelp, and Carrot (200)...1 dish
3. Water Chestnut with Lotus-root Soup (87) ....1 bowl

Heart Disease

The term heart disease can include arteriosclerosis, angina, myocardial infarction (heart attack), stroke, cardiomyopathy, congestive heart failure, heart-valve disease, and other ailments. Though family history is one of the causes, these diseases are often the result of disorderly and unbalanced life styles, especially in regards to food intake.

Arteriosclerosis, for example, is caused by a buildup of fatty deposits (plaque) inside the arteries. The plaque narrows the arteries causing either a decrease in the blood flow or a complete blockage. When this happens, the heart doesn't get the oxygen it needs.

People at the highest risk for this disease are those who are obese, smoke, have a sedentary lifestyle, have a family history of the disease, eat a high-fat diet, and/or have high cholesterol levels (over 230mg/dl). There is no treatment for arteriosclerosis, but if you exercise regularly, reduce the amount of fat in your diet, stop smoking and lower your cholesterol, you will reduce your risk for heart attack.

Master Hou's advises:
1. Eat plain foods. Avoid greasy foods such as high fat meats.
2. Avoid overeating at meal times.
4. Vegetarian foods should dominate in your selections.
5. Rice, wheat, fish, chicken, and lamb are proper foods for those suffering from heart disease. But don't let animal fat exceed 20% of your total caloric intake and 10% of your total fat intake. Never eat high-cholesterol foods like animal organs, egg yolks, shrimp, and lobster.
6. Eat roughly processed rice, wheat flour, and corn; avoid finely processed foods.
7. Eat more fresh vegetables and fruits. In China, we strongly recommend "vegetable cures". We believe this is the best way to lower blood fat and accelerate metabolism.
8. Do more exercises to improve the supply of blood to your heart muscle.

Diet plan for a week
Follow this diet plan for two months. You can vary the actual foods you choose by using this plan, and the other advice I have given you, as a general guideline. Corresponding page numbers are provided for the specific recipes that can be found in this book.

Breakfast

1. Soy milk ....1 glass
2. Sweet and Sour Cucumbers (183) ....1 dish
3. Whole wheat bread ....1 slice

Lunch

1. Vegetable salad ....1 dish
2. Vegetable Fried Rice (238) ....1 dish

Dinner

1. Chinese Cabbage with Mushrooms (165) ....1 dish
2. Pork Spareribs and Kelp Soup (68) ....1 bowl
3. Fruit (an apple, orange, or banana) ....1 piece
4. Steamed rice ....1 bowl

Breakfast

1. Golden Fried Wheat Flour Tea (177) ....1 glass
2. Orange juice..1 glass
3. Fruit (an apple or a banana)......................................1 piece

Lunch

1. Steamed Spinach Noodles (243) ....1 plate
2. Vegetable salad ....1 dish

Dinner

1. Tofu with Green Onion (189)......................................1 dish
2. Mushroom and Garlic (169)..1 dish
3. Fruit (an orange, apple, banana, or kiwi) ....1 piece

Breakfast

1. Oatmeal or grits...1 bowl
2. Fresh carrot juice...1 glass
3. Tea (lemon tea)..1 glass

Lunch

1. Spicy Gingered Chicken (122).....................................1 dish
2. Sandwich (chicken or tuna)..1 piece
3. Fruit (an orange, apple, banana, or kiwi) ....1 cup

Dinner

1. Tomato and Pork Soup (84) ....1 bowl
2. Tofu with Beef (119) ....1 dish
3. Steamed rice ....1 bowl

THURSDAY

Breakfast
1. Soy milk plus and egg white ....1 glass
2. Cucumber with Coriander and Hot Green Pepper (185) ....1 dish
3. Tea or black coffee...1 cup

Lunch
1. White Rice Congee (235) ....1 bowl
2. Scallop Fried Rice (237) ....1 dish
3. Fruit (an orange, apple, banana, or kiwi)..1 piece

Dinner
1. Hot Green Pepper with Potato Strips (208) ....1 dish
2. Spicy Gingered Chicken (122)...1 dish
3. Young Chinese Cabbage and Tofu Soup (88)..1 bowl

FRIDAY

Breakfast
1. White Rice Congee (235) (or a glass of soy milk)...................................1 bowl
2. Spiced-up Celery (190)..1 dish
3. Whole wheat bread ....1 slice
4. Tea (Chrysanthemum Tea (51) or green tea) ....1 cup

Lunch
1. Sandwich (chicken or tuna)..1 sandwich
2. Vegetable salad ....1 dish
3. Fresh carrot juice..1 glass

Dinner
1. Lamb with Carrots (100) ....1 dish
2. Peanuts and Celery (204) ....1 dish
3. Rice (or 1 slice of whole wheat bread) ....1 bowl
4. Bamboo Shoots and Tofu Soup (62) ....1 bowl

SATURDAY

Breakfast
1. Oatmeal or grits..1 bowl
2. Spiced-up Celery (190)..1dish
3. Whole wheat bread ....1 slice

Lunch
1. Pork Chow Mein (241) ....1 dish
2. Fruit (an orange, apple, banana, or kiwi)..1piece
3. Carrot juice..1 glass

Dinner

1. Jellyfish and Turnip (155) ....1 dish
2. Green Bell Pepper with Green Bean Sprouts (197)............................1 dish
3. Soybean and Pork-spareribs Soup (81) ....1 bowl
4. Fruit (your choice)..1 piece

SUNDAY

Breakfast & Lunch

1. Golden Fried Wheat Flour Tea (177) ....1 dish
2. Fruit juice..1 glass
3. Stewed Lamb Rice (239)...1 dish

Dinner

1. Tomato and Pork Soup (84) 1bowl
2. Vegetable salad ....1 dish
3. Fish Fillet with Cucumber (151) ....2 pieces
4. Whole wheat bread ....1 slice

Cancer

Our current understanding of the causes of cancer is incomplete. Cancer develops gradually as a result of a complex mix of factors related to one's environment, lifestyle, and heredity.

There are many factors that are known to increase the risk of cancer, the most common of which are following:

- Tobacco. Tobacco causes cancer. Tobacco use is the most preventable cause of death in this country.
- Diet. Your choice of foods may affect your risk of developing cancer. Evidence points to a link between a high-fat diet and certain cancers, such as cancer of the breast, colon, uterus, and prostate. Being seriously overweight appears to be linked to increased rates of cancer of the prostate, pancreas, uterus, colon, and ovary, as well as breast cancer in older women.
- Sunlight. Ultraviolet radiation from the sun and from other sources (such as sunlamps and tanning booths) damages the skin and can cause skin cancer.
- Alcohol. Drinking large amounts of alcohol increases the risk of cancer of the mouth, throat, esophagus, and larynx. (People who smoke cigarettes and drink alcohol have an especially high risk of getting these cancers.) Alcohol can damage the liver and increase the risk of liver cancer. Some studies suggest that drinking alcohol also increases the risk of breast cancer.
- Radiation. X-rays used for diagnosis expose you to very little radiation, and the benefits nearly always outweigh the risks. Repeated exposure, however, can be harmful, so it is a good idea to talk with your doctor or dentist about the need for each X-ray — and ask about the use of shields to protect other parts of your body.
- Chemicals and other substances in the workplace. Being exposed to substances like metals, dust, chemicals, or pesticides at work can increase the risk of cancer. Asbestos, nickel, cadmium, uranium, radon, vinyl chloride, benzidene, and benzene are other examples of carcinogens in the workplace.

Master Hou's advice:

Cancer is a term used to describe a group of more than 100 different diseases. Here are some general guidelines to follow as preventive measures, and to help regain your health if you do have cancer.

- Studies suggest that foods containing large amounts of fiber and certain nutrients help protect us against some types of cancer. You may be able to reduce your cancer risk by making some simple food choices. Try to have a varied, well-balanced diet that includes generous amounts of foods that are high in fiber, vitamins, and minerals, especially vegetables, fruits, and other plain foods.

- Cut down on fatty foods. You should eat five servings of fruits and vegetables each day. Choose more whole-grain breads and cereals, and cut down on eggs, high-fat meat, high-fat dairy products (such as whole milk, butter, and most cheeses), salad dressings, margarine, and cooking oils.
- Eating well means getting enough calories and protein to help prevent weight loss and regain strength. Patients who eat well during cancer treatment often feel better and have more energy. In addition, they may be better able to handle the side effects of treatment.
- Do not drink alcohol. If you drink at all, do so in moderation — not more than one or two drinks a day.
- Quit smoking.
- Try to avoid pungent foods like ginger, garlic, hot pepper, chives, and some seafood like yellow fish, crab, and shrimp. These foods are believed to cause further deterioration.
- Try to eat organic foods. Many cancers may be the result of chemical substances in foods.

Diet plan for a week

Follow this diet plan for two months. You can vary the actual foods you choose by using this plan, and the other advice I have given you, as a general guideline. Corresponding page numbers are provided for the specific recipes that can be found in this book.

MONDAY

Breakfast

1. Soy milk plus nuts or seeds ....1 glass
2. Sweet and Sour Cucumbers (183) ....1 dish
3. Whole grain bread ....1 slice

Lunch

1. Vegetable salad ....1 dish
2. Vegetable Fried Rice (238) ....1 dish

Dinner

1. Bitter Melon with Soybeans (180) ....1 dish
2. Spareribs with Kelp Soup (68) ....1 bowl
3. Fruit (an apple, orange, or banana) ....1 piece
4. Steamed rice ....1 bowl

TUESDAY

Breakfast

1. Golden Fried Wheat Flour Tea (177) ....1 glass

2. Orange juice..1 glass
3. Fruit (apple or banana)..1 piece

Lunch

1. Steamed Spinach Noodles (243)..1 plate
2. Vegetable salad ....1 dish

Dinner

1. Tofu with Minced Pork (110)..1 dish
2. Herbed Lamb Soup (59) ....1 bowl
3. Steamed rice (or 1 slice of bread) ....1 bowl
4. Fruit (an orange, apple, banana, or kiwi)..1 piece

WEDNESDAY

Breakfast

1. Oatmeal or grits..1 bowl
2. Fresh carrot juice..1 glass

Lunch

1. Sandwich (chicken or tuna)...1 sandwich
2. Fruit (an orange, apple, banana, or kiwi)..1 piece

Dinner

1. Laver, Tofu, and Pork Soup (72) ....1 bowl
2. Vegetable salad ....1 dish
3. Steamed rice ....1 bowl

THURSDAY

Breakfast

1. Soy milk plus one egg white..1 glass
2. Bitter Melon with Soybean (180)..1 dish
3. Whole grain bread...1 slice

Lunch

1. White Rice Congee (235) ....1 bowl
2. Vegetable Fried Rice (238) ....1 dish
3. Fruit (an orange, apple, banana, or kiwi)..1 piece

Dinner

1. Spicy Radishes (212) ....1 dish
2. Young Chinese Cabbage and Tofu Soup (88)..1 bowl
3. Steamed rice ....1 bowl

FRIDAY

Breakfast

1. Soy milk (or 1 bowl of rice) ....1 glass
2. Sesame Celery (178)..1 dish
3. Whole grain bread...1 slice

Lunch

1. Sandwich (chicken or tuna)..1 sandwich
2. Vegetable salad ....1 dish
3. Fresh carrot juice...1 glass

Dinner

1. Lamb with Carrots (100)..1 dish
2. Peanuts and Celery (204)...1 dish
3. Rice (or 1 slice of bread)..1 bowl
4. Pork and Green-bean-sprout Soup (77)..1 bowl

SATURDAY

Breakfast

1. Oatmeal or grits..1 bowl
2. Spiced-up Celery (190)...1 dish
3. Whole wheat bread ....1 slice

Lunch

1. Pork Chow Mein (241)..1 dish
2. Fruit (an orange, apple, banana, or kiwi)......................................1 piece
3. Fresh carrot juice...1 glass

Dinner

1. Crisp Kelp (140) ....1 dish
2. Beef and Spinach Soup (63) ....1 bowl
3. Whole wheat bread ....1 slice
4. Fruit (your choice) ....1 piece

SUNDAY

Breakfast & Lunch

1. Golden Fried Wheat Flour Tea (177) ....1 glass
2. Fruit juice ....1 glass
3. Stewed Lamb Rice (239)..1 dish

Dinner

1. Tomato and Pork Soup (84) ....1 bowl
2. Vegetable salad ....1 dish
3. Fish Fillet with Cucumber (151) ....2 pieces
4. Steamed rice (or 1 slice of bread) ....1 bowl

Arthritis

There are more than 100 different forms of arthritis and many different symptoms and treatments. We do not know what causes most forms of arthritis. Some forms are, however, better understood than others.

Arthritis causes pain and loss of movement and can affect joints in any part of the body. It is usually chronic, meaning it can occur over a long period of time. The more serious forms can cause excessive swelling, warmth, redness, and pain. The three most common kinds of arthritis in older people are osteoarthritis, rheumatoid arthritis and gout.

People taking medicine for any form of arthritis should limit the amount of alcohol they drink.

Exercise, such as a daily walk or swim, helps keep joints moving, reduces pain, and strengthens muscles around the joints. Rest is also important for the joints affected by arthritis. Physical therapists can develop personal programs that balance exercise and rest.

Many people find that soaking in a warm bath, swimming in a heated pool, or applying heat or cold to the area around the joint helps reduce pain. Controlling or losing weight can reduce the stress on joints and can help avoid further damage.

Master Hou's advice:
Osteoarthritis
1. Regular moderate physical activities are advised to help strengthen bone and muscles. Good ones to try are bike riding or swimming in warm water.
2. If you are overweight, try to lose weight to reduce the stress on joints.
3. Do not remain sedentary. Get up and move around if you are sitting at a desk. Take frequent breaks if you are driving long distances.

Rheumatoid Arthritis
Scientists don't know what causes Rheumatoid Arthritis (RA) Researchers theorize that it has something to do with a breakdown in the immune system, the body's defense against disease. It is also likely that people who get RA have certain inherited traits (genes) that cause a disturbance in the immune system

1. There is no effective ways to prevent or cure RA so far.
2. An alcoholic drink can relieve some of the symptoms. The key is moderation. In China, people drink "herb wine" to treat RA.

Gout

1. Keep body weight down, but do not fast because it may cause more uric acid to accumulate.
2. Do not drink alcohol, especially beer. If drinking at all, men should limit themselves to two small glasses and women to one glass.
3. Avoid foods with large amounts of protein, such as animal organs, seafood, or beans.

Unlike the other diseases discussed, arthritis is not as directly related to food intake. The individual characteristics of the specific diseases found under the arthritis umbrella are so different that it is difficult to create a diet plan that would work for all of them. Arranging a diet based on the guidelines given above, while cooperating positively with your doctor is the best solution.

Although I cannot recommend a specific diet plan for arthritis, a number of my recipes do help to relieve symptoms such as painful and swollen joints. Try several and see which ones work best for you.

Resources

The ingredients used in the recipes are common in China. I carefully selected each because of their medicinal value. Many, however, may seem strange or exotic to the average reader. As you prepare to make some of these dishes you may find yourself wondering where to find some of the ingredients.

The simplest and quickest way to find the items on your Chinese food-shopping list is to visit the nearest oriental grocery store. Most towns have at least one oriental food market. Because of the similarity in cuisines between Chinese, Japanese, and Korean, any oriental market should have the ingredients you are looking for. Many larger cities have a Chinatown district you can visit which will have a number of grocery stores to choose from.

If you are having trouble locating an oriental grocery store in your town, or you prefer the convenience of online shopping, please take a look at the following online resources. Several of the resources listed also have information on Asian cooking equipment including steamers and woks.

CTCFood.com

Web site: www.ctcfood.com
Phone: 1-800-356-3134 toll free
This site features quality Asian foods at competitive prices. The wide variety of items they carry include tofu, sesame oil, canned lychee fruit, water chestnuts, and dried mushrooms.

Gongshee.com

Web site: www.gongshee.com
This is a fairly extensive site of Chinese foods and products. Choose the "grocery" link from the pull-down menu for a larger number of choices.

The Oriental Pantry

Web site: www.orientalpantry.com
Phone: 978-264-4576
This is an excellent oriental grocery site with a large selection, including many hard to find items.

AsiaFoods.com

Web site: www.asiafoods.com
This is a comprehensive site including everything from fruits and vegetables to bamboo steamers. If your looking for a hard to find Asian food item your likely to find it here.

Pacificrim-gourmet.com

Web site: www.pacificrim-gourmet.com
Phone: 1-800-618-7575 toll free/916-852-7855 (outside of the US)
This site features Asian-cooking equipment including woks, rice cookers, steamers, spices, and other ingredients.

iKoreaplaza

Website: www.ikoreaplaza.com
Phone: 510-238-8940
This online Korean supermarket carries items you might find on your list including sesame seeds, rice, and beans

Index